# 365

## PERSONAL BRAND

# MARKETING THUMB-RULES™

volume 1

**Daily workbook for rainmakers:**

Lawyers • Accountants • Financial Planners
Real Estate • Health & Wellness professionals

D0109347

# VIKRAM KASAN

CoGrow®

www.MarketingThumbrules.com

365 PERSONAL BRAND Marketing Thumb-rules:
Daily Workbook for Rainmakers, Volume 1
© 2008 Vikram Rajan and CoGrow Systems, Inc.

ISBN 978-0-9797022-1-1

You can also order bulk copies with your own custom cover:

CoGrow Publishing is a division of CoGrow Systems, Inc.
To contact us, please refer to MarketingThumbrules.com
or call (516) 642-4100.

Vikram Rajan is available for speaking, training, & group facilitation.
E-mail Vik@CoGrow.com your inquiry.

*Praise for this book, continued from the back cover:*

Even in today's high-tech world, these marketing basics are still a must. A key component of progress is understanding where you are and where you want to go, which is why measuring your product regularly is so important. I'm so proud that Vikram put this book together. Some of my favorite thumb-rules include # 202, 231, & 279!

**~ Latha Sarathy, Board Member, Volunteer Chair**
*South Asians in Media and Marketing Association*
Director of Research & Analytics, *CBS Digital Media Group*

We all state that we have learned everything in Kindergarden and in the sandbox, but what Vik does best in this book is break all of our thoughts into the simplest logic and implementation. He makes this book fun and inspirational; a winner from page 1.

**~ Bruce Libman, CEO**
*Clients for Life Consulting*

Our community would be more aware, productive and successful when every business practices at least some of these thumb-rules 365 days a year. Some of my favorite thumb-rules are # 11, 28, & 37!

**~ Matt O'Grady, Co-Founder & Associate Publisher**
*Canvas magazine: www.CanvasLI.com*

Master marketer Vik Rajan's new book offers 365 one-page gems designed to set and keep rainmakers on track, with a framework customized (online and in the text) to the needs and predilections of each reader. Although the book is a "quick read," it generates waves of reflective thought and mountains of stimulating ideas. My personal "top 20" favorite thumb-rules were those at pages 33, 71, 87, 134, 154, 183, 201, 283, 291, 296, 298, 301, 305, 314, 316, 324, 336, 349, 356, and 361; my "top two" are on pages 33 and 356.

**~ David J. Abeshouse, Esq., Business Litigator,**
**Arbitrator, & Mediator, *www.BizLawNY.com***
Founder, The Attorney Round Table

If you want to get the most out of your networking relationships, don't just flip through it. Write in this book & share it with others. 2 of our favorite thumb-rules are #3 and #147!

**~ Ellen Volpe & Gene Brown, Partners**
*ABA of Long Island*

In my role as Executive Director of the Queens Medical Society, I often discuss with physicians the need to pro-actively market their practices, as other professionals do. In Vik's book, just about every thumb-rule can be adapted to enhancing a medical practice. In 365 "bite-size" pieces, doctors can become more creative and focused on marketing within the guidelines of the profession and their limited time frames. Thumb-rules 18, 115, 133, and 266 are particularly relevant for physicians and can be used to jumpstart marketing efforts.

**~ Janine Regosin, L.C.S.W., Executive Director**
*The Medical Society of the County of Queens*

Vik, thank you for your guidance and advice as I put my book together. You helped make my book more marketable to other lawyers, accountants, and real estate professionals. Thanks for reinforcing thumb-rules # 79, 113, & 115!

**~ Dennis Haber, Esq., Author**
*Piggy Bank Your Home: Tap Into The Power Of A Reverse Mortgage*

Dentists need to pro-actively market their practices and keep on top of their numbers, like you've helped me to do: That's why I appreciate thumb-rules # 9, 116, & 271.

**~ Dr. Sheri Glazer, DDS, Board Member**
*New York State Academy of General Dentistry*

Since it is 365 rules, I will use it as a calendar and write at the top of each page the month and date.

**~ Karen P. Giunta, CPA, President**
*National Conference of CPA Practitioners*

This is like 365 marketing books in one! Anyone who is serious about marketing their practice should use this book. It makes a great gift for accountants. I especially like thumb-rules #56, 61, 88!

**~ Joseph Tucciarone, Chairman**
*National Network of Accountants*

As CEO of a broker dealer, I find the quotes in this book a wonderful discipline to innovation and self improvement for all professionals in contact with the public. Each day brings new ideas and sparks motivation to improve my business, marketing, time, relationships and life! Thanks Vik for this very useful tool.

**~ Steve Distante, CEO**
*Vanderbilt Securities, LLC.*
President, *National Association of Independent Broker Dealers*

I listen to your audio-books over and over again ... in my car right now!
**~ Geetha Krish, CPA, President**
*Custom Business Services, Inc.*

Your workshop was pertinent and provided us with valuable information to enhance the marketing of our practices as divorce financial planners. I appreciate the significant amount of tools you shared with us as well as your enthusiastic delivery of the materials.
**~ Lili A. Vasileff, CFP®, CDS, CDFA™, President**
*Association of Divorce Financial Planners*

Vik writes the marketing column for us, so you can read the rest of his book in our magazine! Financial service professionals should use these simple, but profound, marketing lessons.
**~ E. Hale Jones, Editor-in-Chief**
*Financial Advisor Publications*

As a Realtor® in residential, commercial and business brokerage and an Adjunct Professor of Real Estate at C.W. Post [Long Island University], recommending Vik's book to all of my clients and students is #1 on my list. As a certified coach to Realtors® nationwide, Thumb-rule #148 has brought me the best results. #19 has been the next most helpful. Everyday is a new thumb-rule to help me succeed.
**~ Gail Gladstone, President**
*www.GailGladstone.com*
President, *Long Island Commercial Network,*
*a division of Long Island Board of Realtors®*

Every professional involved in the real estate world should use this book. Vik, be our featured speaker this year, at the 2008 Expo!
**~ Anthony Kazazis, Founder & Director**
*The Queens Real Estate Expo*

Start using this book right away, whatever time of year, all 365 days. I wish I had this reference when I got my Stanford MBA! Thanks Vikram, you always remind me about thumb-rule #215!
**~ Mahmud 'Wazi' Wazihullah, Managing Partner**
*Commercial Realty Hub*
Membership Director, *Long Island Real Estate Group*

Every business large and small should follow these 365 marketing thumb-rules. Share this book with the entrepreneurs you know. 2 of my favorite thumb-rules are # 158 and # 308.
**~ Mitch Pinckney, Executive Director, Corporate Relations**
*U.S. Chamber of Commerce*

ॐ

Thanks Mom
Thanks Dad

# 365 PERSONAL BRAND Marketing Thumb-rules™

# TABLE OF CONTENTS

# 4 Thumb-rules for Using This Book:

1) Everyday, spend 2 full minutes on 1 thumb-rule: Write.

2) Discuss 1 thumb-rule at your next networking meeting.

3) Discuss 1 thumb-rule at your next team meeting.

4) Go on MarketingThumbrules.com: Add to the blog posts.

## BONUS CHECKLIST #1:
## COMPLIANCE, PROFESSIONALISM & ETHICS

☐ Follow all federal, state, and local laws applicable.

☐ Do not misrepresent yourself, references, or colleagues.

☐ Represent your profession and peers with integrity & class.

☐ Do not make any promises or guarantees of results.

☐ Do not imply specific results through imagery or references.

☐ Do not take money or gifts for referrals, unless within your professional guidelines and a formal partnership contract.

☐ Do not give gifts over $100 or offer money for referrals.

☐ Submit all marketing materials & seminar contents for any applicable compliance and legal review.

☐ Allow at least 2 weeks for your compliance or legal officers to review your marketing matierals.

### CODES OF 'ADVERTISING & MARKETING' ETHICS

☐ **Lawyers**: http://www.abanet.org/abasource/pmm.html

☐ **Certified Public Accountants**: http://www.aicpa.org/about/code/et_502.html#et_502_interpretations

☐ **Certified Financial Planners®**: http://www.cfp.net/Downloads/2008Standards.pdf

☐ **Financial Industry Regulatory Authority** (FINRA): http://finra.complinet.com/finra/display/display_main.html?rbid=118 9&element_id=1159000479

☐ **National Association of Realtors®**: http://www.realtor.org/mempolweb.nsf/pages/code, e.g., Realtors® refers to members of the National Association of Realtors®.

☐ **American Dental Association**: http://www.ada.org/prof/prac/law/code/principles_05.asp

☐ **American Medical Association**: http://www.ama-assn.org/ama/pub/category/2498.html

☐ Also subscribe to MarketingThumbrules.com for insights & ideas.

## BONUS CHECKLIST #2:
## WATERSS: THE 7 PROSPECTING CHANNELS

☐ Word-of-mouth
  ◊ Referrals (clients, prospects, comps)
  ◊ Networking/event prospecting
  ◊ Affiliates/distributors

☐ Advertising/editorial space
  ◊ Print
  ◊ Events
  ◊ Radio
  ◊ Television
  ◊ Complementors' collaterals

☐ Telephone/Fax
  ◊ Cold
  ◊ Warm
  ◊ Automated

☐ Electronic/Internet
  ◊ E-mail
  ◊ SMS (Text msg)
  ◊ RSS

☐ Regular mail
  ◊ Cold
  ◊ Warm

☐ Search/positioning
  ◊ Search engines/portals
  ◊ Directories (YP/association)
  ◊ Tradeshows

☐ Street-based
  ◊ Curb-side
  ◊ On vehicle
  ◊ Door-knocking
  ◊ Guerilla theatre

## BONUS CHECKLIST #3:
## THE 6 TYPES OF MARKETING COLLATERALS

☐ Web-exclusive
  ◊ Forms: Collection focused
  ◊ Blogs: Content focused
  ◊ Portals: Community focused

☐ Audio/visual
  ◊ Logos & jingles
  ◊ Audios (mp3 / audio CD)
  ◊ Videos (Flash / CD/DVD)
  ◊ Slideshows (Web / CD/DVD)
  ◊ Proprietary, neologisms, or associated

☐ Text/printed
  ◊ Postcards
  ◊ Greeting cards
  ◊ Brochures (tri-fold, folders, sales sheets)
  ◊ Newsletters (printed & electronic)
  ◊ Worksheets & checklists
  ◊ Articles, articles, and studies

☐ Events/experiential
  ◊ Seminars & workshops (F2F or tele)
  ◊ Exercises & games (F2F, tele, or asychronous)
  ◊ Socials & parties

☐ Reminders
  ◊ Promotional gifts
  ◊ Branded merchandise

☐ Signage
  ◊ Personal badges
  ◊ Tabletop (booths, stand-alones, etc.)
  ◊ Bumper stickers
  ◊ Wearables
  ◊ Mobile banners (outdoor/indoor)
  ◊ Installed displays

## BONUS CHECKLIST #4:
## THE 7 WEBSITE TRAFFIC DRIVERS

☐ **Subscription contacting**
  ◊ E-mail & RSS
  ◊ SMS txt msg
  ◊ Opt-in automated voice
  ◊ Cooperative blasts

☐ **Site optimization (SEO)**
  ◊ URL/domain name/web address
  ◊ META title, keywords, description
  ◊ Body content (keywords, updates)

☐ **In-links**
  ◊ Reciprocal
  ◊ E-mail signatures
  ◊ Blog comments
  ◊ Profile links (Facebook, LinkedIn, ActiveRain, etc.)
  ◊ Directory listings

☐ **Sponsored search / Pay-Per-Click**
  ◊ Keywords (Google, Yahoo!, MSN, etc.)
  ◊ Site specific (communities, affiliates)
  ◊ Re-directs

☐ **Banner display advertising**
  ◊ Text
  ◊ Image
  ◊ Audio/video
  ◊ Pop-ups & pop-unders

☐ **Product-specific**
  ◊ Affiliates, distributors, re-sellers, pay-per-close
  ◊ Auctions (eBay, verticals)
  ◊ Classifieds (Craigslist, Google Base)
  ◊ Storefronts (Amazon, B&N, verticals)

☐ **Off-line channels: W.A.T.E.R.S.S.**

## BONUS CHECKLIST #5:
## THE 6 AREAS OF WEB PRESENCE

☐ **Credential/company sites**
   ◊ About your competencies/expertise
   ◊ Announcements, news, & coverage
   ◊ Partner & personnel backgrounds

☐ **Capture/contact sites**
   ◊ Forms, forms, forms (e-mail contact)
   ◊ Public profiles of visitors ('members')
   ◊ Private access to special content

☐ **Content/blog sites**
   ◊ E-newsletter
   ◊ Articles, images, audios, & videos
   ◊ Comments & forums

☐ **Campaign/copyright sites**
   ◊ Search terms
   ◊ Names, titles, slogans, brands
   ◊ Product specific

☐ **Portal profiles/posts**
   ◊ Product listings: eBay, Craigslist
   ◊ Networking: LinkedIn, Facebook, etc.
   ◊ Expertise: Yahoo! Answers, verticals

☐ **Off-line collaterals**
   ◊ W.A.T.E.R.S.

## BONUS CHECKLIST #6:
## THE 7 CURRENTS OF BUZZ

☐ **Star Power**
 ◊ Name-drop well-known clients
 ◊ Name-drop well-known association positions
 ◊ Encourage well-known people to mention your name
 ◊ Encourage well-known associations to mention you

☐ **Dates & Calendar**
 ◊ Seasonal and/or repeated events & gatherings
 ◊ Mainstream & popular holidays
 ◊ Your own special dates & times

☐ **Lingo, Buzzwords, & Colloquialisms**
 ◊ Zeitgeist headlines and market slang
 ◊ Industry jargon, acronyms, and phrases
 ◊ Well-known authors, leaders, and institutions

☐ **Statistics & Numbers**
 ◊ Studies & surveys
 ◊ Lists & rosters
 ◊ Percentages & ratios
 ◊ Graphs & charts

☐ **Pollination & Viral marketing**
 ◊ Riders and tags
 ◊ Branded merchandise or gifts
 ◊ Incentives for word-of-mouth or closing

☐ **Contradiction & Controversy**
 ◊ Counter to generally accepted practices or beliefs
 ◊ Debates, arguments, disagreements, and fights
 ◊ Sub-cultures, counter cultures, & alternatively-proud
 ◊ Secrets, codes/ciphers, and elite reservations

☐ **Nicknames & Labels**
 ◊ Honorable & earned titles of recognition
 ◊ Middle-names & catchphrases
 ◊ Just first OR last, in place of full name

## BONUS CHECKLIST #7:
## THE 6 TARGETS OF COMMUNITY MARKETS

☐ **Label awareness (Group consciousness)**
◊ Do their common characteristics have a name?
◊ Do they describe themselves with a group term?
◊ Would they publicly admit to what you ascribe?

☐ **Felt, pressured, and urgent need**
◊ Government mandate or regulatary pressure
◊ Peer pressure; from trusted advisors, or influencers
◊ Seasonal or date-driven deadline

☐ **Lingo and dates**
◊ Jargon & colloquialisms
◊ Personal interests & hobbies
◊ Events, conferences, & gatherings

☐ **Media subscriptions**
◊ Event attendance
◊ Readership: Magazines, journals, newspapers, etc.
◊ Websites, portals, blogs, etc.

☐ **Preferred buying channels**
◊ Which one of the W.A.T.E.R.S.S. do they prefer?
◊ Who do they ask? Who are their top influencers?
◊ How do they learn about what you know?
◊ Where do they buy complementary services?

☐ **Personal Brand appeal**
◊ What makes your competency different and better?
◊ What makes your character distinctive and better?
◊ What makes your charisma distinctive and better?
◊ Who says, besides you?

## 1 Sample Thumb-rule Journal Page

> # Journal solo or
> # Brainstorm as a group.

*How important is this thumb-rule to you?* ★ ★ ★ ★ ☆

*What's your experience with this thumb-rule into your day? Share it here:*

This would definitely make my networking group become more productive. Each rule of thumb is a great discussion starter. We can go around and ask each other if and where we'd heard of the thumb-rule, from whom... and how we implement the thumb-rule in our businesses. We can share each others' marketing ideas that way! And do more business with each other!!

ACTION ITEMS:

- Write out comments for each day's thumb-rule.

- Bring this book to my next networking meeeting.

- Go to the book's website and share comments.

*How well do you practice this thumb-rule?* low 1 2 3 (4) 5 6 high

For explanations, anecdotes, and book recommendations, go to *MarketingThumbrules.com* & type in these keyword tags:
Consistency, leadership, people, networking, events, time

Practice **Management** Thumb-rule #1

> # The only thing worse than your business being dependent on you, is your business being dependent on somebody else.

*How important is this thumb-rule to you?* ☆ ☆ ☆ ☆ ☆

*How will you incorporate this thumb-rule into your day? Journal it here:*

ACTION ITEMS:

*How well do you practice this thumb-rule?* low 1 2 3 4 5 6 high

For explanations, anecdotes, and book recommendations, go to *MarketingThumbrules.com* & type in these keyword tags: Controls, leadership, people, delegation, system

Practice **Management** Thumb-rule #2

# Lead by example.
# Practice what you preach.

*How important is this thumb-rule to you?* ☆ ☆ ☆ ☆ ☆

*What's your experience with this thumb-rule? Write it below:*

ACTION ITEMS:

*How well do you practice this thumb-rule?* low 1  2  3  4  5  6  high

For explanations, anecdotes, and book recommendations,
go to *MarketingThumbrules.com* & type in these keyword tags:
Character, Charisma, leadership, reputation, delegation

Practice **Management** Thumb–rule #3

> # You can do anything,
> # just not everything.

*How important is this thumb-rule to you?* ☆ ☆ ☆ ☆ ☆

*How will you incorporate this thumb-rule into your day? Journal it here:*

---

ACTION ITEMS:

---

*How well do you practice this thumb-rule?* low 1 2 3 4 5 6 high

For explanations, anecdotes, and book recommendations,
go to *MarketingThumbrules.com* & type in these keyword tags:
Controls, Character, leadership, prioritize, time

Practice **Management** Thumb-rule #4

# What you put in, is what you get out. (G.I.G.O.)

*How important is this thumb-rule to you?* ☆ ☆ ☆ ☆ ☆

*What's your experience with this thumb-rule? Write it below:*

ACTION ITEMS:

*How well do you practice this thumb-rule?* low 1 2 3 4 5 6 high

For explanations, anecdotes, and book recommendations, go to *MarketingThumbrules.com* & type in these keyword tags: Controls, Consistency, experience, system

Practice **Management** Thumb–rule #5

# Leverage:
# Do a little, gain a lot.

*How important is this thumb-rule to you?* ☆ ☆ ☆ ☆ ☆

*How will you incorporate this thumb-rule into your day? Journal it here:*

ACTION ITEMS:

*How well do you practice this thumb-rule?* low 1 2 3 4 5 6 high

For explanations, anecdotes, and book recommendations,
go to *MarketingThumbrules.com* & type in these keyword tags:
Controls, prioritize, time, results

Practice **Management** Thumb-rule #6

## Delay, delete, delegate then Do.

*How important is this thumb-rule to you?* ☆ ☆ ☆ ☆ ☆

*What's your experience with this thumb-rule? Write it below:*

ACTION ITEMS:

*How well do you practice this thumb-rule?* low 1 2 3 4 5 6 high

For explanations, anecdotes, and book recommendations, go to *MarketingThumbrules.com* & type in these keyword tags: Controls, delegation, prioritize, time, system, results, planning

Practice **Management** Thumb–rule #7

> # There is no long-term,
> # without the short-term.

*How important is this thumb-rule to you?* ☆ ☆ ☆ ☆ ☆

*How will you incorporate this thumb-rule into your day? Journal it here:*

---

---

---

---

ACTION ITEMS:

---

---

*How well do you practice this thumb-rule?* low  1  2  3  4  5  6  high

For explanations, anecdotes, and book recommendations,
go to *MarketingThumbrules.com* & type in these keyword tags:
Controls, planning, results

Practice **Management** Thumb–rule #8

# WYSIWYG.

*How important is this thumb-rule to you?* ☆ ☆ ☆ ☆ ☆

*What's your experience with this thumb-rule? Write it below:*

ACTION ITEMS:

*How well do you practice this thumb-rule?* low 1 2 3 4 5 6 high

For explanations, anecdotes, and book recommendations, go to *MarketingThumbrules.com* & type in these keyword tags: Charisma, planning, goals, vision, mindset, results

Practice **Management** Thumb–rule #9

> # Don't focus on the past,
> # because you cannot change it.
> # Focus on the future.

*How important is this thumb-rule to you?* ☆ ☆ ☆ ☆ ☆

*How will you incorporate this thumb-rule into your day? Journal it here:*

---

---

---

---

ACTION ITEMS:

---

---

*How well do you practice this thumb-rule?* low 1  2   3  4   5  6  high

For explanations, anecdotes, and book recommendations,
go to *MarketingThumbrules.com* & type in these keyword tags:
Charisma, Character, mindset, planning, vision

Practice **Management** Thumb–rule #10

## Work the 80/20 principle.

*How important is this thumb-rule to you?* ☆ ☆ ☆ ☆ ☆

*What's your experience with this thumb-rule?* *Write it below:*

..............................................................................................................

..............................................................................................................

..............................................................................................................

..............................................................................................................

ACTION ITEMS:

..............................................................................................................

..............................................................................................................

*How well do you practice this thumb-rule?* low 1  2  3  4  5  6  high

For explanations, anecdotes, and book recommendations, go to *MarketingThumbrules.com* & type in these keyword tags: Controls, prioritize, results

Practice **Management** Thumb-rule #11

## Practice the Golden Rule.

*How important is this thumb-rule to you?* ☆ ☆ ☆ ☆ ☆

*How will you incorporate this thumb-rule into your day? Journal it here:*

---

---

---

---

ACTION ITEMS:

---

---

*How well do you practice this thumb-rule?* low 1 2 3 4 5 6 high

For explanations, anecdotes, and book recommendations,
go to *MarketingThumbrules.com* & type in these keyword tags:
Character, leadership, values, people, delegation, relationships

Practice **Management** Thumb-rule #12

> # Nurture good people.
> # Be willing to pay them more.

*How important is this thumb-rule to you?* ☆ ☆ ☆ ☆ ☆

*What's your experience with this thumb-rule? Write it below:*

ACTION ITEMS:

*How well do you practice this thumb-rule?* low 1 2 3 4 5 6 high

For explanations, anecdotes, and book recommendations,
go to *MarketingThumbrules.com* & type in these keyword tags:
Controls, people, leadership, delegation

Practice **Management** Thumb-rule #13

> # A change in one area
> # will always impact another.

*How important is this thumb-rule to you?* ☆ ☆ ☆ ☆ ☆

*How will you incorporate this thumb-rule into your day? Journal it here:*

---

---

---

---

ACTION ITEMS:

---

---

*How well do you practice this thumb-rule?* low 1  2  3  4  5  6  high

For explanations, anecdotes, and book recommendations,
go to *MarketingThumbrules.com* & type in these keyword tags:
Controls, leadership, system, results

Practice **Management** Thumb–rule #14

## Your vision illuminates the opportunities around you.

*How important is this thumb-rule to you?* ☆ ☆ ☆ ☆ ☆

*What's your experience with this thumb-rule? Write it below:*

........................................................................................................

........................................................................................................

........................................................................................................

........................................................................................................

ACTION ITEMS:

........................................................................................................

........................................................................................................

*How well do you practice this thumb-rule?* low 1 2 3 4 5 6 high

For explanations, anecdotes, and book recommendations, go to *MarketingThumbrules.com* & type in these keyword tags: Charisma, vision, planning, results

Practice **Management** Thumb-rule #15

> # As soon as you feel you don't need any more positive mindset support, that's precisely when you need more.

*How important is this thumb-rule to you?* ☆ ☆ ☆ ☆ ☆

*How will you incorporate this thumb-rule into your day? Journal it here:*

_____

_____

_____

_____

ACTION ITEMS:

_____

_____

*How well do you practice this thumb-rule?* low 1 2 3 4 5 6 high

For explanations, anecdotes, and book recommendations, go to *MarketingThumbrules.com* & type in these keyword tags: Character, Charisma, leadership, values, mindset

Practice **Management** Thumb-rule #16

> # Any system that isn't flexible for people will collapse.

*How important is this thumb-rule to you?* ☆ ☆ ☆ ☆ ☆

*What's your experience with this thumb-rule? Write it below:*

ACTION ITEMS:

*How well do you practice this thumb-rule?* low 1 2 3 4 5 6 high

For explanations, anecdotes, and book recommendations, go to *MarketingThumbrules.com* & type in these keyword tags: Controls, people, system, delegation, results

Practice **Management** Thumb–rule #17

# Write down your action goals, not just your result goals.

*How important is this thumb-rule to you?* ☆ ☆ ☆ ☆ ☆

*How will you incorporate this thumb-rule into your day? Journal it here:*

ACTION ITEMS:

*How well do you practice this thumb-rule?* low 1 2 3 4 5 6 high

For explanations, anecdotes, and book recommendations, go to *MarketingThumbrules.com* & type in these keyword tags: Controls, Consistency, planning, goals, results

Practice **Management** Thumb–rule #18

> # We don't find time. We have to make the time: Schedule it.

*How important is this thumb-rule to you?* ☆ ☆ ☆ ☆ ☆

*What's your experience with this thumb-rule? Write it below:*

--------------------------------------------------

--------------------------------------------------

--------------------------------------------------

--------------------------------------------------

ACTION ITEMS:

--------------------------------------------------

--------------------------------------------------

*How well do you practice this thumb-rule?* low 1  2  3  4  5  6  high

For explanations, anecdotes, and book recommendations, go to *MarketingThumbrules.com* & type in these keyword tags:
Controls, Consistency, time, planning, results

Practice **Management** Thumb-rule #19

# Clear your desk to clear your mind.

*How important is this thumb-rule to you?* ☆ ☆ ☆ ☆ ☆

*How will you incorporate this thumb-rule into your day? Journal it here:*

ACTION ITEMS:

*How well do you practice this thumb-rule?* low 1 2 3 4 5 6 high

For explanations, anecdotes, and book recommendations, go to *MarketingThumbrules.com* & type in these keyword tags: Charisma, Character, Controls, mindset, prioritize

Practice **Management** Thumb–rule #20

> # Plan your next vacation.

*How important is this thumb-rule to you?* ☆ ☆ ☆ ☆ ☆

*What's your experience with this thumb-rule? Write it below:*

ACTION ITEMS:

*How well do you practice this thumb-rule?* low  1   2   3   4   5   6  high

For explanations, anecdotes, and book recommendations,
go to *MarketingThumbrules.com* & type in these keyword tags:
Character, planning, mindset, values

Practice **Management** Thumb-rule #21

## Clearly stipulate short deadlines.

*How important is this thumb-rule to you?* ☆ ☆ ☆ ☆ ☆

*How will you incorporate this thumb-rule into your day? Journal it here:*

ACTION ITEMS:

*How well do you practice this thumb-rule?* low 1 2 3 4 5 6 high

For explanations, anecdotes, and book recommendations,
go to *MarketingThumbrules.com* & type in these keyword tags:
Controls, leadership, people, delegation, results

Practice **Management** Thumb–rule #22

# Leadership is taken, not given.

*How important is this thumb-rule to you?* ☆ ☆ ☆ ☆ ☆

*What's your experience with this thumb-rule? Write it below:*

ACTION ITEMS:

*How well do you practice this thumb-rule?* low 1 2 3 4 5 6 high

For explanations, anecdotes, and book recommendations,
go to *MarketingThumbrules.com* & type in these keyword tags:
Charisma, Character, leadership, results

Practice **Management** Thumb–rule #23

## Let go ...

*How important is this thumb-rule to you?* ☆ ☆ ☆ ☆ ☆

*How will you incorporate this thumb-rule into your day? Journal it here:*

-----

-----

-----

-----

ACTION ITEMS:

-----

-----

*How well do you practice this thumb-rule?* low 1 2 3 4 5 6 high

For explanations, anecdotes, and book recommendations,
go to *MarketingThumbrules.com* & type in these keyword tags:
Charisma, leadership, people, delegation

Practice **Management** Thumb–rule #24

> # Don't over-help (e.g., chick in egg): Help others to help themselves.

*How important is this thumb-rule to you?* ☆ ☆ ☆ ☆ ☆

*What's your experience with this thumb-rule? Write it below:*

ACTION ITEMS:

*How well do you practice this thumb-rule?* low 1 2 3 4 5 6 high

For explanations, anecdotes, and book recommendations, go to *MarketingThumbrules.com* & type in these keyword tags:
Character, Controls, leadership, people, relationships

Practice **Management** Thumb-rule #25

> # Write down a 'to-do' list.

*How important is this thumb-rule to you?* ☆ ☆ ☆ ☆ ☆

*How will you incorporate this thumb-rule into your day? Journal it here:*

ACTION ITEMS:

*How well do you practice this thumb-rule?* low 1 2 3 4 5 6 high

For explanations, anecdotes, and book recommendations,
go to *MarketingThumbrules.com* & type in these keyword tags:
Controls, time, prioritize, results

Practice **Management** Thumb-rule #26

## Ask your kids to teach you about new technology.

*How important is this thumb-rule to you?* ☆ ☆ ☆ ☆ ☆

*What's your experience with this thumb-rule? Write it below:*

ACTION ITEMS:

*How well do you practice this thumb-rule?* low 1 2 3 4 5 6 high

For explanations, anecdotes, and book recommendations, go to *MarketingThumbrules.com* & type in these keyword tags: Competency, questions, innovation, technology

Practice **Management** Thumb-rule #27

## Procrastinate later.

*How important is this thumb-rule to you?* ☆ ☆ ☆ ☆ ☆

*How will you incorporate this thumb-rule into your day? Journal it here:*

ACTION ITEMS:

*How well do you practice this thumb-rule?* low 1 2 3 4 5 6 high

For explanations, anecdotes, and book recommendations, go to *MarketingThumbrules.com* & type in these keyword tags: Character, Controls, time, results

Practice **Management** Thumb–rule #28

# Lend books to others.
## Put your contact information on it.
## But don't expect them back.

*How important is this thumb-rule to you?* ☆ ☆ ☆ ☆ ☆

*What's your experience with this thumb-rule? Write it below:*

ACTION ITEMS:

*How well do you practice this thumb-rule?* low 1  2  3  4  5  6  high

For explanations, anecdotes, and book recommendations,
go to *MarketingThumbrules.com* & type in these keyword tags:
Competency, Channels, Controls, people

Practice **Management** Thumb–rule #29

## Nobody likes being told they're wrong.

*How important is this thumb-rule to you?* ☆ ☆ ☆ ☆ ☆

*How will you incorporate this thumb-rule into your day? Journal it here:*

ACTION ITEMS:

*How well do you practice this thumb-rule?* low 1 2 3 4 5 6 high

For explanations, anecdotes, and book recommendations,
go to *MarketingThumbrules.com* & type in these keyword tags:
Character, Charisma, people, relationships

Practice **Management** Thumb–rule #30

## Save money.

*How important is this thumb-rule to you?* ☆ ☆ ☆ ☆ ☆

*What's your experience with this thumb-rule? Write it below:*

ACTION ITEMS:

*How well do you practice this thumb-rule?* low 1 2 3 4 5 6 high

For explanations, anecdotes, and book recommendations, go to *MarketingThumbrules.com* & type in these keyword tags: Controls, money, planning

Practice **Management** Thumb–rule #31

> # Don't become a neat freak.
> # Make money & hire people
> # to organize your world.

*How important is this thumb-rule to you?* ☆ ☆ ☆ ☆ ☆

*How will you incorporate this thumb-rule into your day? Journal it here:*

--------------------------------------------------------------------

--------------------------------------------------------------------

--------------------------------------------------------------------

--------------------------------------------------------------------

ACTION ITEMS:

--------------------------------------------------------------------

--------------------------------------------------------------------

*How well do you practice this thumb-rule?* low 1  2  3  4  5  6  high

For explanations, anecdotes, and book recommendations,
go to *MarketingThumbrules.com* & type in these keyword tags:
Character, prioritize, delegation, mindset, values

Practice **Management** Thumb–rule #32

> # Just rip off the bandage!
> # It hurts less than brooding about it.

*How important is this thumb-rule to you?* ☆ ☆ ☆ ☆ ☆

*What's your experience with this thumb-rule? Write it below:*

ACTION ITEMS:

*How well do you practice this thumb-rule?* low 1 2 3 4 5 6 high

For explanations, anecdotes, and book recommendations, go to *MarketingThumbrules.com* & type in these keyword tags: Controls, prioritize, results

Practice **Management** Thumb-rule #33

> # Busy people get things done.
> # Give it to a busy person.

*How important is this thumb-rule to you?* ☆ ☆ ☆ ☆ ☆

*How will you incorporate this thumb-rule into your day? Journal it here:*

ACTION ITEMS:

*How well do you practice this thumb-rule?* low 1 2 3 4 5 6 high

For explanations, anecdotes, and book recommendations,
go to *MarketingThumbrules.com* & type in these keyword tags:
Character, Channels, delegation, leadership, results

Practice **Management** Thumb–rule #34

**Get back to the basics.**

*How important is this thumb-rule to you?* ☆ ☆ ☆ ☆ ☆

*What's your experience with this thumb-rule? Write it below:*

ACTION ITEMS:

*How well do you practice this thumb-rule?* low 1 2 3 4 5 6 high

For explanations, anecdotes, and book recommendations, go to *MarketingThumbrules.com* & type in these keyword tags: Competency, Competency, planning, goals, results

Practice **Management** Thumb-rule #35

**Discipline.**

*How important is this thumb-rule to you?* ☆ ☆ ☆ ☆ ☆

*How will you incorporate this thumb-rule into your day? Journal it here:*

ACTION ITEMS:

*How well do you practice this thumb-rule?* low 1 2 3 4 5 6 high

For explanations, anecdotes, and book recommendations,
go to *MarketingThumbrules.com* & type in these keyword tags:
Controls, leadership, people, results, goals

Practice **Management** Thumb-rule #36

## Visualize success through pictures and role models.

*How important is this thumb-rule to you?* ☆ ☆ ☆ ☆ ☆

*What's your experience with this thumb-rule? Write it below:*

....................................................................................

....................................................................................

....................................................................................

....................................................................................

ACTION ITEMS:

....................................................................................

....................................................................................

*How well do you practice this thumb-rule?* low 1 2 3 4 5 6 high

For explanations, anecdotes, and book recommendations, go to *MarketingThumbrules.com* & type in these keyword tags: Charisma, Character, vision, values

Practice **Management** Thumb–rule #37

> # *Stop looking for the 'ANY' key.*
> # *Click around; experiment.*
> # *It won't blow up... most likely.*

*How important is this thumb-rule to you?* ☆ ☆ ☆ ☆ ☆

*How will you incorporate this thumb-rule into your day? Journal it here:*

-------------------------------------------------------------

-------------------------------------------------------------

-------------------------------------------------------------

-------------------------------------------------------------

ACTION ITEMS:

-------------------------------------------------------------

-------------------------------------------------------------

*How well do you practice this thumb-rule?* low  1  2  3  4  5  6  high

For explanations, anecdotes, and book recommendations,
go to *MarketingThumbrules.com* & type in these keyword tags:
Competency, Controls, technology, experience

Practice **Management** Thumb-rule #38

> # Install virus protection software, spyware remover, registry cleaner, and a fire wall.

*How important is this thumb-rule to you?* ☆ ☆ ☆ ☆ ☆

*What's your experience with this thumb-rule? Write it below:*

ACTION ITEMS:

*How well do you practice this thumb-rule?* low 1 2 3 4 5 6 high

For explanations, anecdotes, and book recommendations, go to *MarketingThumbrules.com* & type in these keyword tags: Controls, technology, planning

Practice **Management** Thumb-rule #39

# Back up your hard drive continually.

*How important is this thumb-rule to you?* ☆ ☆ ☆ ☆ ☆

*How will you incorporate this thumb-rule into your day? Journal it here:*

ACTION ITEMS:

*How well do you practice this thumb-rule?* low 1 2 3 4 5 6 high

For explanations, anecdotes, and book recommendations,
go to *MarketingThumbrules.com* & type in these keyword tags:
Controls, technology, planning

Practice **Management** Thumb–rule #40

# When life gives you lemons, make lemonade.

*How important is this thumb-rule to you?* ☆ ☆ ☆ ☆ ☆

*What's your experience with this thumb-rule? Write it below:*

ACTION ITEMS:

*How well do you practice this thumb-rule?* low 1 2 3 4 5 6 high

For explanations, anecdotes, and book recommendations,
go to *MarketingThumbrules.com* & type in these keyword tags:
Controls, Character, smile, mindset, results, compliance

Practice **Management** Thumb–rule #41

> # Surround yourself
> # with people smarter than you.

*How important is this thumb-rule to you?* ☆ ☆ ☆ ☆ ☆

*How will you incorporate this thumb-rule into your day? Journal it here:*

ACTION ITEMS:

*How well do you practice this thumb-rule?* low 1  2  3  4  5  6  high

For explanations, anecdotes, and book recommendations,
go to *MarketingThumbrules.com* & type in these keyword tags:
Competency, Character, people, relationships, delegation

Practice **Management** Thumb-rule #42

> ## Just because it worked for someone else, that doesn't mean it will work for you.

*How important is this thumb-rule to you?* ☆ ☆ ☆ ☆ ☆

*What's your experience with this thumb-rule? Write it below:*

.................................................................................................

.................................................................................................

.................................................................................................

.................................................................................................

ACTION ITEMS:

.................................................................................................

.................................................................................................

*How well do you practice this thumb-rule?* low 1 2 3 4 5 6 high

For explanations, anecdotes, and book recommendations, go to *MarketingThumbrules.com* & type in these keyword tags: Controls, experience, planning, results

Practice **Management** Thumb–rule #43

# Sandwich bad news or criticisms between 2 positive comments.

*How important is this thumb-rule to you?* ☆ ☆ ☆ ☆ ☆

*How will you incorporate this thumb-rule into your day? Journal it here:*

---

---

---

---

ACTION ITEMS:

---

---

*How well do you practice this thumb-rule?* low 1  2  3  4  5  6  high

For explanations, anecdotes, and book recommendations, go to *MarketingThumbrules.com* & type in these keyword tags: Charisma, leadership, people, delegation

Practice **Management** Thumb–rule #44

> # It takes 21 days to make a habit.
> # It takes 100 days to gain real results.

*How important is this thumb-rule to you?* ☆ ☆ ☆ ☆ ☆

*What's your experience with this thumb-rule? Write it below:*

ACTION ITEMS:

*How well do you practice this thumb-rule?* low 1 2 3 4 5 6 high

For explanations, anecdotes, and book recommendations, go to *MarketingThumbrules.com* & type in these keyword tags: Character, Consistency, experience, results, mindset

Practice **Management** Thumb-rule #45

## Don't do Paper-Time work during your Prime Time.

How important is this thumb-rule to you? ☆ ☆ ☆ ☆ ☆

How will you incorporate this thumb-rule into your day? Journal it here:

ACTION ITEMS:

How well do you practice this thumb-rule? low 1 2 3 4 5 6 high

For explanations, anecdotes, and book recommendations,
go to *MarketingThumbrules.com* & type in these keyword tags:
Controls, compliance, time, prioritize, results

Practice **Management** Thumb-rule #46

> ## Your family is more important than any business meeting.

*How important is this thumb-rule to you?* ☆ ☆ ☆ ☆ ☆

*What's your experience with this thumb-rule? Write it below:*

ACTION ITEMS:

*How well do you practice this thumb-rule?* low 1 2 3 4 5 6 high

For explanations, anecdotes, and book recommendations,
go to *MarketingThumbrules.com* & type in these keyword tags:
Character, prioritize, values, mindset

Practice **Management** Thumb–rule #47

> # Together Everybody Achieves More, so long as each member feels as such.

*How important is this thumb-rule to you?* ☆ ☆ ☆ ☆ ☆

*How will you incorporate this thumb-rule into your day? Journal it here:*

---

---

---

---

ACTION ITEMS:

---

---

*How well do you practice this thumb-rule?* low 1 2 3 4 5 6 high

For explanations, anecdotes, and book recommendations, go to *MarketingThumbrules.com* & type in these keyword tags: Charisma, leadership, people, relationships, delegation

Practice **Management** Thumb-rule #48

## Make a small mess first, then clean it up.

*How important is this thumb-rule to you?* ☆ ☆ ☆ ☆ ☆

*What new ideas does this thumb-rule inspire? Write it down quickly:*

ACTION ITEMS:

*How well do you practice this thumb-rule?* low 1 2 3 4 5 6 high

For explanations, anecdotes, and book recommendations,
go to *MarketingThumbrules.com* & type in these keyword tags:
Controls, results, experience, planning

Practice **Management** Thumb–rule #49

> ## *Carry this book around:*
> ## Focus your marketing in the
> ## nooks & crannies of your day.

*How important is this thumb-rule to you?* ☆ ☆ ☆ ☆ ☆

*How will you incorporate this thumb-rule into your day? Journal it here:*

---

---

---

---

ACTION ITEMS:

---

---

*How well do you practice this thumb-rule?* low 1 2 3 4 5 6 high

For explanations, anecdotes, and book recommendations,
go to *MarketingThumbrules.com* & type in these keyword tags:
Competency, prioritize, time

Practice **Management** Thumb-rule #50

## Begin with the end goal in mind.

*How important is this thumb-rule to you?* ☆ ☆ ☆ ☆ ☆

*What new ideas does this thumb-rule inspire? Write it down quickly:*

ACTION ITEMS:

*How well do you practice this thumb-rule?* low 1 2 3 4 5 6 high

For explanations, anecdotes, and book recommendations,
go to *MarketingThumbrules.com* & type in these keyword tags:
Controls, planning, goals, vision, prioritize

Market **Positioning** Thumb-rule #1

## Target an overlooked market.

*How important is this thumb-rule to you?* ☆ ☆ ☆ ☆ ☆

*How many versions of this thumb-rule can you express? Share it here:*

---

---

---

---

ACTION ITEMS:

---

---

*How well do you practice this thumb-rule?* low 1 2 3 4 5 6 high

For explanations, anecdotes, and book recommendations, go to *MarketingThumbrules.com* & type in these keyword tags: Community, competition

Market **Positioning** Thumb-rule #2

# Divide & conquer.

*How important is this thumb-rule to you?* ☆ ☆ ☆ ☆ ☆

*What new ideas does this thumb-rule inspire? Write it down quickly:*

ACTION ITEMS:

*How well do you practice this thumb-rule?* low 1 2 3 4 5 6 high

For explanations, anecdotes, and book recommendations,
go to *MarketingThumbrules.com* & type in these keyword tags:
Community, competition

Market **Positioning** Thumb–rule #3

## To sustain & duplicate your marketing success you need to control the variables.

*How important is this thumb-rule to you?* ☆ ☆ ☆ ☆ ☆

*How many versions of this thumb-rule can you express? Share it here:*

-----------------------------------------------------------

-----------------------------------------------------------

-----------------------------------------------------------

-----------------------------------------------------------

-----------------------------------------------------------

ACTION ITEMS:

-----------------------------------------------------------

-----------------------------------------------------------

*How well do you practice this thumb-rule?* low 1 2 3 4 5 6 high

For explanations, anecdotes, and book recommendations, go to *MarketingThumbrules.com* & type in these keyword tags: Controls, results

Market **Positioning** Thumb–rule #4

> # Don't go after a disappearing market.

*How important is this thumb-rule to you?* ☆ ☆ ☆ ☆ ☆

*What new ideas does this thumb-rule inspire? Write it down quickly:*

ACTION ITEMS:

*How well do you practice this thumb-rule?* low 1 2 3 4 5 6 high

For explanations, anecdotes, and book recommendations, go to *MarketingThumbrules.com* & type in these keyword tags: Community, Channels, Controls

Market **Positioning** Thumb-rule #5

---

# It's better to get 1% from 100 sources, than 100% from only 1 source.

---

*How important is this thumb-rule to you?* ☆ ☆ ☆ ☆ ☆

*How many versions of this thumb-rule can you express? Share it here:*

ACTION ITEMS:

*How well do you practice this thumb-rule?* low 1 2 3 4 5 6 high

For explanations, anecdotes, and book recommendations, go to *MarketingThumbrules.com* & type in these keyword tags: Controls, results, mindset, relationships

Market **Positioning** Thumb–rule #6

## You can make every threat into your opportunity.

*How important is this thumb-rule to you?* ☆ ☆ ☆ ☆ ☆

*What new ideas does this thumb-rule inspire? Write it down quickly:*

ACTION ITEMS:

*How well do you practice this thumb-rule?* low 1 2 3 4 5 6 high

For explanations, anecdotes, and book recommendations, go to *MarketingThumbrules.com* & type in these keyword tags: Character, Controls, mindset, vision, planning

Market **Positioning** Thumb-rule #7

# Learn from your direct competition and your indirect competition.

*How important is this thumb-rule to you?* ☆ ☆ ☆ ☆ ☆

*How many versions of this thumb-rule can you express? Share it here:*

---

---

---

---

ACTION ITEMS:

---

---

*How well do you practice this thumb-rule?* low 1 2 3 4 5 6 high

For explanations, anecdotes, and book recommendations, go to *MarketingThumbrules.com* & type in these keyword tags: Competency, competition

Market **Positioning** Thumb-rule #8

> ## 'The whole' should be greater than 'the sum of its parts'.

*How important is this thumb-rule to you?* ☆ ☆ ☆ ☆ ☆

*What new ideas does this thumb-rule inspire? Write it down quickly:*

ACTION ITEMS:

*How well do you practice this thumb-rule?* low 1 2 3 4 5 6 high

For explanations, anecdotes, and book recommendations, go to **MarketingThumbrules.com** & type in these keyword tags: Controls, mindset, system

Market **Positioning** Thumb-rule #9

---

# *Decision means 'to cut off'.* Decision-making means being willing to make mistakes.

---

*How important is this thumb-rule to you?* ☆ ☆ ☆ ☆ ☆

*How many versions of this thumb-rule can you express? Share it here:*

---

---

---

---

ACTION ITEMS:

---

---

*How well do you practice this thumb-rule?* low 1 2 3 4 5 6 high

For explanations, anecdotes, and book recommendations, go to *MarketingThumbrules.com* & type in these keyword tags: Controls, mindset, values, planning

Market **Positioning** Thumb–rule #10

> # A chain, or system, is
> # only as strong as its weakest link.

*How important is this thumb-rule to you?* ☆ ☆ ☆ ☆ ☆

*What new ideas does this thumb-rule inspire? Write it down quickly:*

-----

-----

-----

-----

ACTION ITEMS:

-----

-----

*How well do you practice this thumb-rule?* low 1 2 3 4 5 6 high

For explanations, anecdotes, and book recommendations, go to *MarketingThumbrules.com* & type in these keyword tags: Controls, system, relationships

Market **Positioning** Thumb-rule #11

## Cooperate & Grow.

*How important is this thumb-rule to you?* ☆ ☆ ☆ ☆ ☆

*How many versions of this thumb-rule can you express? Share it here:*

ACTION ITEMS:

*How well do you practice this thumb-rule?* low 1 2 3 4 5 6 high

For explanations, anecdotes, and book recommendations, go to *MarketingThumbrules.com* & type in these keyword tags: Character, relationships, mindset

Market **Positioning** Thumb-rule #12

## Don't kill the goose that lays the golden eggs. *Don't bite the hand that feeds you.*

*How important is this thumb-rule to you?* ☆ ☆ ☆ ☆ ☆

*What new ideas does this thumb-rule inspire? Write it down quickly:*

ACTION ITEMS:

*How well do you practice this thumb-rule?* low 1 2 3 4 5 6 high

For explanations, anecdotes, and book recommendations, go to *MarketingThumbrules.com* & type in these keyword tags: Controls, experience, relationships, results

Market **Positioning** Thumb-rule #13

## Excite your environment.

*How important is this thumb-rule to you?* ☆ ☆ ☆ ☆ ☆

*How many versions of this thumb-rule can you express? Share it here:*

ACTION ITEMS:

*How well do you practice this thumb-rule?* low 1 2 3 4 5 6 high

For explanations, anecdotes, and book recommendations, go to *MarketingThumbrules.com* & type in these keyword tags: Charisma, Character, leadership, people, values, mindset

Market **Positioning** Thumb–rule #14

## What makes you distinctive beyond your credentials, experience, customer service, or rates?

*How important is this thumb-rule to you?* ☆ ☆ ☆ ☆ ☆

*What new ideas does this thumb-rule inspire? Write it down quickly:*

ACTION ITEMS:

*How well do you practice this thumb-rule?* low 1 2 3 4 5 6 high

For explanations, anecdotes, and book recommendations, go to *MarketingThumbrules.com* & type in these keyword tags: Competency, Character, reputation, competition, experience

Market **Positioning** Thumb–rule #15

> # David can't beat Goliath by doing what Goliath does to beat David.

*How important is this thumb-rule to you?* ☆ ☆ ☆ ☆ ☆

*How many versions of this thumb-rule can you express? Share it here:*

------------------------------------------------

------------------------------------------------

------------------------------------------------

------------------------------------------------

ACTION ITEMS:

------------------------------------------------

------------------------------------------------

*How well do you practice this thumb-rule?* low 1 2 3 4 5 6 high

For explanations, anecdotes, and book recommendations, go to *MarketingThumbrules.com* & type in these keyword tags: Channels, competition, reputation, planning

Market **Positioning** Thumb–rule #16

# Set S.M.A.R.T. goals that stretch you.

*How important is this thumb-rule to you?* ☆ ☆ ☆ ☆ ☆

*What new ideas does this thumb-rule inspire? Write it down quickly:*

ACTION ITEMS:

*How well do you practice this thumb-rule?* low  1  2  3  4  5  6  high

For explanations, anecdotes, and book recommendations,
go to *MarketingThumbrules.com* & type in these keyword tags:
Controls, Character, goals, vision, planning

Market **Positioning** Thumb–rule #17

> # If you're everything to everybody, then you're nothing to nobody.

*How important is this thumb-rule to you?* ☆ ☆ ☆ ☆ ☆

*How many versions of this thumb-rule can you express? Share it here:*

------------------------------------------------------

------------------------------------------------------

------------------------------------------------------

------------------------------------------------------

ACTION ITEMS:

------------------------------------------------------

------------------------------------------------------

*How well do you practice this thumb-rule?* low 1  2  3  4  5  6  high

For explanations, anecdotes, and book recommendations,
go to *MarketingThumbrules.com* & type in these keyword tags:
Community, reputation, competition

Market **Positioning** Thumb–rule #18

## A 10 year old should understand what you do & why clients buy.

*How important is this thumb-rule to you?* ☆ ☆ ☆ ☆ ☆

*What new ideas does this thumb-rule inspire? Write it down quickly:*

ACTION ITEMS:

*How well do you practice this thumb-rule?* low 1 2 3 4 5 6 high

For explanations, anecdotes, and book recommendations, go to *MarketingThumbrules.com* & type in these keyword tags: Controls, message, reputation, competition

Market **Positioning** Thumb-rule #19

> # Have persistence toward the end, not the means.

*How important is this thumb-rule to you?* ☆ ☆ ☆ ☆ ☆

*How many versions of this thumb-rule can you express? Share it here:*

---

---

---

---

ACTION ITEMS:

---

---

*How well do you practice this thumb-rule?* low 1 2 3 4 5 6 high

For explanations, anecdotes, and book recommendations, go to *MarketingThumbrules.com* & type in these keyword tags: Controls, planning, goals, results

Market **Positioning** Thumb-rule #20

# As soon as you have a worthwhile goal, life will get in the way. Plan & act accordingly.

*How important is this thumb-rule to you?* ☆ ☆ ☆ ☆ ☆

*What new ideas does this thumb-rule inspire? Write it down quickly:*

ACTION ITEMS:

*How well do you practice this thumb-rule?* low 1 2 3 4 5 6 high

For explanations, anecdotes, and book recommendations, go to *MarketingThumbrules.com* & type in these keyword tags: Controls, planning, goals, mindset

Market **Positioning** Thumb-rule #21

> # It's better to do a few things great, than many things average.

*How important is this thumb-rule to you?* ☆ ☆ ☆ ☆ ☆

*How many versions of this thumb-rule can you express? Share it here:*

ACTION ITEMS:

*How well do you practice this thumb-rule?* low 1 2 3 4 5 6 high

For explanations, anecdotes, and book recommendations,
go to *MarketingThumbrules.com* & type in these keyword tags:
Competency, reputation, experience, leadership, results, time

Market **Positioning** Thumb–rule #22

# Learn from other people's mistakes. And your own.

*How important is this thumb-rule to you?*  ☆ ☆ ☆ ☆ ☆

*What new ideas does this thumb-rule inspire? Write it down quickly:*

---

ACTION ITEMS:

---

*How well do you practice this thumb-rule?* low 1 2 3 4 5 6 high

For explanations, anecdotes, and book recommendations,
go to *MarketingThumbrules.com* & type in these keyword tags:
Competency, planning, results, competition, people

Market **Positioning** Thumb–rule #23

# The more specific the demographic profile, the more predictable the psychographic behavior.

*How important is this thumb-rule to you?* ☆ ☆ ☆ ☆ ☆

*How many versions of this thumb-rule can you express? Share it here:*

---

---

---

---

ACTION ITEMS:

---

---

*How well do you practice this thumb-rule?* low  1  2  3  4  5  6  high

For explanations, anecdotes, and book recommendations, go to *MarketingThumbrules.com* & type in these keyword tags: Community, mindset, people

Market **Positioning** Thumb–rule #24

# Ride the wave.
# Make a splash if you want to pioneer.

*How important is this thumb-rule to you?* ☆ ☆ ☆ ☆ ☆

*What new ideas does this thumb-rule inspire? Write it down quickly:*

ACTION ITEMS:

*How well do you practice this thumb-rule?* low 1 2 3 4 5 6 high

For explanations, anecdotes, and book recommendations,
go to *MarketingThumbrules.com* & type in these keyword tags:
Community, Currency, competition, message

Market **Positioning** Thumb–rule #25

## K.I.S.S.
## Keep it Short & Simple.

*How important is this thumb-rule to you?* ☆ ☆ ☆ ☆ ☆

*How many versions of this thumb-rule can you express? Share it here:*

----

----

----

----

ACTION ITEMS:

----

----

*How well do you practice this thumb-rule?* low 1 2 3 4 5 6 high

For explanations, anecdotes, and book recommendations, go to *MarketingThumbrules.com* & type in these keyword tags: Collaterals, Consistency, message, system

Market **Positioning** Thumb-rule #26

# Perception is reality.

*How important is this thumb-rule to you?* ☆ ☆ ☆ ☆ ☆

*What new ideas does this thumb-rule inspire? Write it down quickly:*

ACTION ITEMS:

*How well do you practice this thumb-rule?* low 1 2 3 4 5 6 high

For explanations, anecdotes, and book recommendations, go to *MarketingThumbrules.com* & type in these keyword tags: Charisma, competition, message, people, vision, leadership

Market **Positioning** Thumb-rule #27

> # Focus your energy
> # like a magnifying glass.

*How important is this thumb-rule to you?* ☆ ☆ ☆ ☆ ☆

*How many versions of this thumb-rule can you express? Share it here:*

ACTION ITEMS:

*How well do you practice this thumb-rule?* low 1 2 3 4 5 6 high

For explanations, anecdotes, and book recommendations, go to *MarketingThumbrules.com* & type in these keyword tags:
Controls, time, prioritize, mindset, planning

Market **Positioning** Thumb–rule #28

# Win / Win.

*How important is this thumb-rule to you?* ☆ ☆ ☆ ☆ ☆

*What new ideas does this thumb-rule inspire? Write it down quickly:*

ACTION ITEMS:

*How well do you practice this thumb-rule?* low 1  2  3  4  5  6  high

For explanations, anecdotes, and book recommendations, go to *MarketingThumbrules.com* & type in these keyword tags: Character, leadership, people, reputation, values, mindset

Market **Positioning** Thumb–rule #29

## Copyright, trademark, and '.com', your special phrases.

*How important is this thumb-rule to you?* ☆ ☆ ☆ ☆ ☆

*How many versions of this thumb-rule can you express? Share it here:*

ACTION ITEMS:

*How well do you practice this thumb-rule?* low 1 2 3 4 5 6 high

For explanations, anecdotes, and book recommendations, go to *MarketingThumbrules.com* & type in these keyword tags: Controls, planning, system, wealth

Market **Positioning** Thumb–rule #30

# Use pictures:
# They're worth a thousand words.

*How important is this thumb-rule to you?* ☆ ☆ ☆ ☆ ☆

*What new ideas does this thumb-rule inspire? Write it down quickly:*

ACTION ITEMS:

*How well do you practice this thumb-rule?* low 1 2 3 4 5 6 high

For explanations, anecdotes, and book recommendations, go to *MarketingThumbrules.com* & type in these keyword tags: Collaterals, Currency, Consistency

Market **Positioning** Thumb–rule #31

**Prioritize the big blocks first.**

*How important is this thumb-rule to you?* ☆ ☆ ☆ ☆ ☆

*How many versions of this thumb-rule can you express? Share it here:*

ACTION ITEMS:

*How well do you practice this thumb-rule?* low 1  2  3  4  5  6  high

For explanations, anecdotes, and book recommendations,
go to *MarketingThumbrules.com* & type in these keyword tags:
Controls, time, prioritize, planning

Market **Positioning** Thumb-rule #32

> # Be the exception to the rule.
> # Take common practice,
> # and do the opposite.

*How important is this thumb-rule to you?* ☆ ☆ ☆ ☆ ☆

*What new ideas does this thumb-rule inspire? Write it down quickly:*

ACTION ITEMS:

*How well do you practice this thumb-rule?* low 1 2 3 4 5 6 high

For explanations, anecdotes, and book recommendations,
go to *MarketingThumbrules.com* & type in these keyword tags:
Contros, Character, leadership, competition, system, mindset

Market **Positioning** Thumb–rule #33

# Remember your local library offers 'free' services (that you've paid for).

*How important is this thumb-rule to you?* ☆ ☆ ☆ ☆ ☆

*How many versions of this thumb-rule can you express? Share it here:*

-----------------------------------------------------------------

-----------------------------------------------------------------

-----------------------------------------------------------------

-----------------------------------------------------------------

ACTION ITEMS:

-----------------------------------------------------------------

-----------------------------------------------------------------

*How well do you practice this thumb-rule?* low 1 2 3 4 5 6 high

For explanations, anecdotes, and book recommendations, go to *MarketingThumbrules.com* & type in these keyword tags: Competency, technology, people, publishing

Market **Positioning** Thumb-rule #34

> # Write out the steps of your efforts to improve it and delegate it.

*How important is this thumb-rule to you?* ☆ ☆ ☆ ☆ ☆

*What new ideas does this thumb-rule inspire? Write it down quickly:*

ACTION ITEMS:

*How well do you practice this thumb-rule?* low 1 2 3 4 5 6 high

For explanations, anecdotes, and book recommendations, go to *MarketingThumbrules.com* & type in these keyword tags: Controls, leadership, system, delegation, people

Market **Positioning** Thumb-rule #35

# Write easy-to-follow time-lines on a monthly wall calendar.

*How important is this thumb-rule to you?* ☆ ☆ ☆ ☆ ☆

*How many versions of this thumb-rule can you express? Share it here:*

ACTION ITEMS:

*How well do you practice this thumb-rule?* low 1 2 3 4 5 6 high

For explanations, anecdotes, and book recommendations, go to *MarketingThumbrules.com* & type in these keyword tags: Controls, system, planning, events

Market **Positioning** Thumb–rule #36

> # Those who teach learn twice as much.
> ## *And position themselves as experts.*

*How important is this thumb-rule to you?* ☆ ☆ ☆ ☆ ☆

*What new ideas does this thumb-rule inspire? Write it down quickly:*

ACTION ITEMS:

*How well do you practice this thumb-rule?* low 1 2 3 4 5 6 high

For explanations, anecdotes, and book recommendations,
go to *MarketingThumbrules.com* & type in these keyword tags:
Competency, reputation, events

Market **Positioning** Thumb–rule #37

## Actions speak louder than words: Proof is in the pudding.

*How important is this thumb-rule to you?* ☆ ☆ ☆ ☆ ☆

*How many versions of this thumb-rule can you express? Share it here:*

---

---

---

---

ACTION ITEMS:

---

---

*How well do you practice this thumb-rule?* low 1 2 3 4 5 6 high

For explanations, anecdotes, and book recommendations, go to *MarketingThumbrules.com* & type in these keyword tags: Controls, results

Market **Positioning** Thumb-rule #38

## Write down all your ideas.
## Share it only with trusted advisors.

*How important is this thumb-rule to you?* ☆ ☆ ☆ ☆ ☆

*What new ideas does this thumb-rule inspire? Write it down quickly:*

ACTION ITEMS:

*How well do you practice this thumb-rule?* low 1 2 3 4 5 6 high

For explanations, anecdotes, and book recommendations,
go to *MarketingThumbrules.com* & type in these keyword tags:
Controls, wealth, innovation

Market **Positioning** Thumb–rule #39

> # 2 mediocres don't make a great.

*How important is this thumb-rule to you?* ☆ ☆ ☆ ☆ ☆

*How many versions of this thumb-rule can you express? Share it here:*

---

---

---

---

ACTION ITEMS:

---

---

*How well do you practice this thumb-rule?* low 1  2  3  4  5  6 high

For explanations, anecdotes, and book recommendations, go to *MarketingThumbrules.com* & type in these keyword tags: Controls, people, relationships

Market **Positioning** Thumb-rule #40

## Continuously improve.

*How important is this thumb-rule to you?* ☆ ☆ ☆ ☆ ☆

*What new ideas does this thumb-rule inspire? Write it down quickly:*

ACTION ITEMS:

*How well do you practice this thumb-rule?* low 1 2 3 4 5 6 high

For explanations, anecdotes, and book recommendations, go to *MarketingThumbrules.com* & type in these keyword tags: Controls, Consistency, system, innovation

Market **Positioning** Thumb-rule #41

**People value expensive things more.**

*How important is this thumb-rule to you?* ☆ ☆ ☆ ☆ ☆

*How many versions of this thumb-rule can you express? Share it here:*

ACTION ITEMS:

*How well do you practice this thumb-rule?* low 1  2  3  4  5  6  high

For explanations, anecdotes, and book recommendations,
go to *MarketingThumbrules.com* & type in these keyword tags:
Community, Currency, people, money, competition

Market **Positioning** Thumb–rule #42

# The Textbook can't replace The Street.

*How important is this thumb-rule to you?* ☆ ☆ ☆ ☆ ☆

*What new ideas does this thumb-rule inspire? Write it down quickly:*

ACTION ITEMS:

*How well do you practice this thumb-rule?* low 1 2 3 4 5 6 high

For explanations, anecdotes, and book recommendations,
go to *MarketingThumbrules.com* & type in these keyword tags:
Competency, Character, experience, people, publishing

Market **Positioning** Thumb–rule #43

> # If you can't beat 'em, make money off 'em.

*How important is this thumb-rule to you?*  ☆ ☆ ☆ ☆ ☆

*How many versions of this thumb-rule can you express? Share it here:*

ACTION ITEMS:

*How well do you practice this thumb-rule?* low 1 2 3 4 5 6 high

For explanations, anecdotes, and book recommendations, go to *MarketingThumbrules.com* & type in these keyword tags: Controls, competition, money, relationships

Market **Positioning** Thumb-rule #44

## Headlines are less than 7 words.

*How important is this thumb-rule to you?* ☆ ☆ ☆ ☆ ☆

*What new ideas does this thumb-rule inspire? Write it down quickly:*

ACTION ITEMS:

*How well do you practice this thumb-rule?* low 1 2 3 4 5 6 high

For explanations, anecdotes, and book recommendations, go to *MarketingThumbrules.com* & type in these keyword tags: Collaterals, catchphrase, message, publishing

Market **Positioning** Thumb–rule #45

## Cross-promote & reference your events, articles, and other products.

*How important is this thumb-rule to you?* ☆ ☆ ☆ ☆ ☆

*How many versions of this thumb-rule can you express? Share it here:*

---

ACTION ITEMS:

---

*How well do you practice this thumb-rule?* low 1 2 3 4 5 6 high

For explanations, anecdotes, and book recommendations, go to *MarketingThumbrules.com* & type in these keyword tags: Channels, reputation, wealth, publishing, events

Market **Positioning** Thumb-rule #46

## Supply & Demand rules.

*How important is this thumb-rule to you?* ☆ ☆ ☆ ☆ ☆

*What new ideas does this thumb-rule inspire? Write it down quickly:*

ACTION ITEMS:

*How well do you practice this thumb-rule?* low 1 2 3 4 5 6 high

For explanations, anecdotes, and book recommendations,
go to *MarketingThumbrules.com* & type in these keyword tags:
Controls, competition, people

Market **Positioning** Thumb–rule #47

## Advertise charitable donations made from sales.

*How important is this thumb-rule to you?* ☆ ☆ ☆ ☆ ☆

*How many versions of this thumb-rule can you express? Share it here:*

ACTION ITEMS:

*How well do you practice this thumb-rule?* low 1  2  3  4  5  6  high

For explanations, anecdotes, and book recommendations, go to *MarketingThumbrules.com* & type in these keyword tags: Character, wealth, values, message

Market **Positioning** Thumb-rule #48

## Keep great marketing materials, for future design reference.

*How important is this thumb-rule to you?* ☆ ☆ ☆ ☆ ☆

*What new ideas does this thumb-rule inspire? Write it down quickly:*

ACTION ITEMS:

*How well do you practice this thumb-rule?* low 1 2 3 4 5 6 high

For explanations, anecdotes, and book recommendations, go to *MarketingThumbrules.com* & type in these keyword tags: Collaterals, competition, message

Market **Positioning** Thumb-rule #49

## How can you turn competitors into clients?

*How important is this thumb-rule to you?* ☆ ☆ ☆ ☆ ☆

*How many versions of this thumb-rule can you express? Share it here:*

ACTION ITEMS:

*How well do you practice this thumb-rule?* low 1 2 3 4 5 6 high

For explanations, anecdotes, and book recommendations, go to *MarketingThumbrules.com* & type in these keyword tags: Community, competition, innovation, questions

Market **Positioning** Thumb–rule #50

## Create < 10 word catchphrases that others can repeat in their vernacular.

*How important is this thumb-rule to you?* ☆ ☆ ☆ ☆ ☆

*What new ideas does this thumb-rule inspire? Write it down quickly:*

ACTION ITEMS:

*How well do you practice this thumb-rule?* low 1 2 3 4 5 6 high

For explanations, anecdotes, and book recommendations, go to *MarketingThumbrules.com* & type in these keyword tags:
Collaterals, catchphrase, message

Market **Positioning** Thumb-rule #51

> # Subscribe to the magazines subscribed by your target market.

*How important is this thumb-rule to you?* ☆ ☆ ☆ ☆ ☆

*How many versions of this thumb-rule can you express? Share it here:*

--------------------------------------------------------------

--------------------------------------------------------------

--------------------------------------------------------------

--------------------------------------------------------------

ACTION ITEMS:

--------------------------------------------------------------

--------------------------------------------------------------

*How well do you practice this thumb-rule?* low 1 2 3 4 5 6 high

For explanations, anecdotes, and book recommendations,
go to *MarketingThumbrules.com* & type in these keyword tags:
Community, Competency, publishing

Market **Positioning** Thumb-rule #52

## Become a big fish in a small pond... then only jump into a bigger pond.

*How important is this thumb-rule to you?* ☆ ☆ ☆ ☆ ☆

*What new ideas does this thumb-rule inspire? Write it down quickly:*

ACTION ITEMS:

*How well do you practice this thumb-rule?* low 1 2 3 4 5 6 high

For explanations, anecdotes, and book recommendations, go to *MarketingThumbrules.com* & type in these keyword tags: Community, competition, goals

Market **Positioning** Thumb–rule #53

# Become a profit-sharing affiliate of complementary products. (Disclose when you recommend.)

*How important is this thumb-rule to you?* ☆ ☆ ☆ ☆ ☆

*How many versions of this thumb-rule can you express? Share it here:*

---

---

---

---

ACTION ITEMS:

---

---

*How well do you practice this thumb-rule?* low 1 2 3 4 5 6 high

For explanations, anecdotes, and book recommendations, go to *MarketingThumbrules.com* & type in these keyword tags: Controls, wealth, relationships, affiliates

Market **Positioning** Thumb-rule #54

## 20% of your clients may be outside your target market.

*How important is this thumb-rule to you?* ☆ ☆ ☆ ☆ ☆

*What new ideas does this thumb-rule inspire? Write it down quickly:*

----------------------------------------

----------------------------------------

----------------------------------------

----------------------------------------

ACTION ITEMS:

----------------------------------------

----------------------------------------

*How well do you practice this thumb-rule?* low 1 2 3 4 5 6 high

For explanations, anecdotes, and book recommendations, go to *MarketingThumbrules.com* & type in these keyword tags: Community, relationships

Market **Positioning** Thumb-rule #55

> # A non-profit can own a for-profit.
> # A for-profit cannot own a non-profit.

*How important is this thumb-rule to you?* ☆ ☆ ☆ ☆ ☆

*How many versions of this thumb-rule can you express? Share it here:*

_____

_____

_____

_____

ACTION ITEMS:

_____

_____

*How well do you practice this thumb-rule?* low 1 2 3 4 5 6 high

For explanations, anecdotes, and book recommendations, go to *MarketingThumbrules.com* & type in these keyword tags: Controls, innovation, money

Market **Positioning** Thumb-rule #56

> # Build residual income
> ## - like retainers & subscriptions -
> ## so you don't start from 0 each month.

*How important is this thumb-rule to you?*  ☆ ☆ ☆ ☆ ☆

*What new ideas does this thumb-rule inspire? Write it down quickly:*

---

---

---

---

ACTION ITEMS:

---

---

*How well do you practice this thumb-rule?*  low 1  2  3  4  5  6  high

For explanations, anecdotes, and book recommendations,
go to *MarketingThumbrules.com* & type in these keyword tags:
Controls, money, publishing

Market **Positioning** Thumb–rule #57

> # Preach to the choir.
> # Let 'em convert their circle of influence.

*How important is this thumb-rule to you?* ☆ ☆ ☆ ☆ ☆

*How many versions of this thumb-rule can you express? Share it here:*

ACTION ITEMS:

*How well do you practice this thumb-rule?* low 1 2 3 4 5 6 high

For explanations, anecdotes, and book recommendations,
go to *MarketingThumbrules.com* & type in these keyword tags:
Community, people, catchphrase

Market **Positioning** Thumb–rule #58

> # Target 2 markets: Retail = end-users.
> # Wholesale = distributors & referrers.

*How important is this thumb-rule to you?* ☆ ☆ ☆ ☆ ☆

*What new ideas does this thumb-rule inspire? Write it down quickly:*

........................................................................................

........................................................................................

........................................................................................

........................................................................................

........................................................................................

ACTION ITEMS:

........................................................................................

........................................................................................

*How well do you practice this thumb-rule?* low 1 2 3 4 5 6 high

For explanations, anecdotes, and book recommendations,
go to *MarketingThumbrules.com* & type in these keyword tags:
Community, people, reputation, affiliates

Personal **Branding** Thumb–rule #1

---

# Don't believe your own hype.
# Stay humble.

---

*How important is this thumb-rule to you?* ☆ ☆ ☆ ☆ ☆

*How will you improve your practice with this thumb-rule? Affirm it here:*

---

ACTION ITEMS:

---

*How well do you practice this thumb-rule?* low 1 2 3 4 5 6 high

For explanations, anecdotes, and book recommendations,
go to *MarketingThumbrules.com* & type in these keyword tags:
Character, reputation, mindset, values

Personal **Branding** Thumb-rule #2

## Register *yourname.com* and multiple domains with non-abbreviated keywords.

*How important is this thumb-rule to you?* ☆ ☆ ☆ ☆ ☆

*How have other colleagues showcased this thumb-rule? Write it below:*

------------------------------------------------

------------------------------------------------

------------------------------------------------

------------------------------------------------

------------------------------------------------

ACTION ITEMS:

------------------------------------------------

------------------------------------------------

*How well do you practice this thumb-rule?* low 1 2 3 4 5 6 high

For explanations, anecdotes, and book recommendations, go to *MarketingThumbrules.com* & type in these keyword tags: Collaterals, message, catchphrase, technology

Personal **Branding** Thumb–rule #3

## Your habits = Your destiny.

*How important is this thumb-rule to you?* ☆ ☆ ☆ ☆ ☆

*How will you improve your practice with this thumb-rule? Affirm it here.*

ACTION ITEMS:

*How well do you practice this thumb-rule?* low 1  2  3  4  5  6 high

For explanations, anecdotes, and book recommendations,
go to *MarketingThumbrules.com* & type in these keyword tags:
Character, Consistency, values, results

Personal **Branding** Thumb-rule #4

# Your practice cannot sustain growth beyond your self-image.

*How important is this thumb-rule to you?* ☆ ☆ ☆ ☆ ☆

*How have other colleagues showcased this thumb-rule? Write it below:*

ACTION ITEMS:

*How well do you practice this thumb-rule?* low 1 2 3 4 5 6 high

For explanations, anecdotes, and book recommendations, go to *MarketingThumbrules.com* & type in these keyword tags: Charisma, mindset, values, results

Personal **Branding** Thumb-rule #5

> # Every week, post 3 times on your blog and 3 comments on others'.

*How important is this thumb-rule to you?* ☆ ☆ ☆ ☆ ☆

*How will you improve your practice with this thumb-rule? Affirm it here.*

ACTION ITEMS:

*How well do you practice this thumb-rule?* low 1 2 3 4 5 6 high

For explanations, anecdotes, and book recommendations, go to *MarketingThumbrules.com* & type in these keyword tags: Channels, Consistency, message, technology

Personal **Branding** Thumb-rule #6

# Repeat your catchphrases.
# Stay on message.

*How important is this thumb-rule to you?* ☆ ☆ ☆ ☆ ☆

*How have other colleagues showcased this thumb-rule? Write it below:*

. . . . . . . . . . . . . . . . . . . . . . . . . . . . . . . . . . . . . . . . . . . . . . . . . . . . . . .

. . . . . . . . . . . . . . . . . . . . . . . . . . . . . . . . . . . . . . . . . . . . . . . . . . . . . . .

. . . . . . . . . . . . . . . . . . . . . . . . . . . . . . . . . . . . . . . . . . . . . . . . . . . . . . .

. . . . . . . . . . . . . . . . . . . . . . . . . . . . . . . . . . . . . . . . . . . . . . . . . . . . . . .

ACTION ITEMS:

. . . . . . . . . . . . . . . . . . . . . . . . . . . . . . . . . . . . . . . . . . . . . . . . . . . . . . .

. . . . . . . . . . . . . . . . . . . . . . . . . . . . . . . . . . . . . . . . . . . . . . . . . . . . . . .

*How well do you practice this thumb-rule?* low 1  2  3  4  5  6 high

For explanations, anecdotes, and book recommendations,
go to *MarketingThumbrules.com* & type in these keyword tags:
Consistency, Collaterals, message, catchphrase

Personal **Branding** Thumb–rule #7

## Publish articles.

*How important is this thumb-rule to you?* ☆ ☆ ☆ ☆ ☆

*How will you improve your practice with this thumb-rule? Affirm it here.*

ACTION ITEMS:

*How well do you practice this thumb-rule?* low 1　2　3　4　5　6　high

For explanations, anecdotes, and book recommendations,
go to *MarketingThumbrules.com* & type in these keyword tags:
Collaterals, publishing, reputation, wealth

Personal **Branding** Thumb–rule #8

# Pause & smile.

*How important is this thumb-rule to you?* ☆ ☆ ☆ ☆ ☆

*How have other colleagues showcased this thumb-rule? Write it below:*

ACTION ITEMS:

*How well do you practice this thumb-rule?* low 1 2 3 4 5 6 high

For explanations, anecdotes, and book recommendations, go to *MarketingThumbrules.com* & type in these keyword tags: Character, Charisma, reputation, values, mindset

Personal **Branding** Thumb-rule #9

# Match & mirror speech and body language to help build rapport.

*How important is this thumb-rule to you?* ☆ ☆ ☆ ☆ ☆

*How will you improve your practice with this thumb-rule? Affirm it here:*

---

---

---

---

ACTION ITEMS:

---

---

*How well do you practice this thumb-rule?* low 1 2 3 4 5 6 high

For explanations, anecdotes, and book recommendations, go to *MarketingThumbrules.com* & type in these keyword tags: Charisma, people, relationships

Personal **Branding** Thumb-rule #10

## Start where you are.
## Take consistent baby steps.

*How important is this thumb-rule to you?* ☆ ☆ ☆ ☆ ☆

*How have other colleagues showcased this thumb-rule? Write it below:*

ACTION ITEMS:

*How well do you practice this thumb-rule?* low 1 2 3 4 5 6 high

For explanations, anecdotes, and book recommendations,
go to *MarketingThumbrules.com* & type in these keyword tags:
Controls, results, prioritize

Personal **Branding** Thumb–rule #11

## Method = Message.
## How you say it is just as
## important as what you're saying.

*How important is this thumb-rule to you?* ☆ ☆ ☆ ☆ ☆

*How will you improve your practice with this thumb-rule? Affirm it here:*

ACTION ITEMS:

*How well do you practice this thumb-rule?* low 1  2  3  4  5  6  high

For explanations, anecdotes, and book recommendations,
go to *MarketingThumbrules.com* & type in these keyword tags:
Character, leadership, message, people

Personal **Branding** Thumb-rule #12

# Nobody cares how much you know until they know how much you care.

*How important is this thumb-rule to you?* ☆ ☆ ☆ ☆ ☆

*How have other colleagues showcased this thumb-rule? Write it below:*

ACTION ITEMS:

*How well do you practice this thumb-rule?* low 1 2 3 4 5 6 high

For explanations, anecdotes, and book recommendations, go to *MarketingThumbrules.com* & type in these keyword tags: Charisma, leadership, people, relationships, values, mindset

Personal **Branding** Thumb-rule #13

## Smile at others.
## Laugh at yourself.

*How important is this thumb-rule to you?* ☆ ☆ ☆ ☆ ☆

*How will you improve your practice with this thumb-rule? Affirm it here.*

ACTION ITEMS:

*How well do you practice this thumb-rule?* low  1   2   3   4   5   6  high

For explanations, anecdotes, and book recommendations,
go to *MarketingThumbrules.com* & type in these keyword tags:
Character, smile, relationships, people

Personal **Branding** Thumb-rule #14

# Fake it 'til you make it.

*How important is this thumb-rule to you?* ☆ ☆ ☆ ☆ ☆

*How have other colleagues showcased this thumb-rule? Write it below:*

ACTION ITEMS:

*How well do you practice this thumb-rule?* low 1 2 3 4 5 6 high

For explanations, anecdotes, and book recommendations,
go to *MarketingThumbrules.com* & type in these keyword tags:
Character, results

Personal **Branding** Thumb–rule #15

> # Recite affirmations:
> ## Say what you want that you don't have;
> ## not what you don't want, that you do have.

*How important is this thumb-rule to you?* ☆ ☆ ☆ ☆ ☆

*How will you improve your practice with this thumb-rule? Affirm it here.*

---

---

---

---

ACTION ITEMS:

---

---

*How well do you practice this thumb-rule?* low 1  2  3  4  5  6  high

For explanations, anecdotes, and book recommendations,
go to *MarketingThumbrules.com* & type in these keyword tags:
Charisma, mindset, goals

Personal **Branding** Thumb-rule #16

## Productize your expertise.

*How important is this thumb-rule to you?* ☆ ☆ ☆ ☆ ☆

*How have other colleagues showcased this thumb-rule? Write it below:*

ACTION ITEMS:

*How well do you practice this thumb-rule?* low 1 2 3 4 5 6 high

For explanations, anecdotes, and book recommendations,
go to *MarketingThumbrules.com* & type in these keyword tags:
Competency, Collaterals, publishing, wealth

Personal **Branding** Thumb-rule #17

# Be consistent with your keywords, colors, images, and actions.

*How important is this thumb-rule to you?* ☆ ☆ ☆ ☆ ☆

*How will you improve your practice with this thumb-rule? Affirm it here:*

ACTION ITEMS:

*How well do you practice this thumb-rule?* low  1  2  3  4  5  6  high

For explanations, anecdotes, and book recommendations, go to *MarketingThumbrules.com* & type in these keyword tags: Collaterals, Consistency, catchphrase, message

Personal **Branding** Thumb–rule #18

> # To encourage memory & response, create a multi-sensory experience.

*How important is this thumb-rule to you?* ☆ ☆ ☆ ☆ ☆

*How have other colleagues showcased this thumb-rule? Write it below:*

------------------------------------------------------------

------------------------------------------------------------

------------------------------------------------------------

------------------------------------------------------------

------------------------------------------------------------

ACTION ITEMS:

------------------------------------------------------------

------------------------------------------------------------

*How well do you practice this thumb-rule?* low 1 2 3 4 5 6 high

For explanations, anecdotes, and book recommendations, go to *MarketingThumbrules.com* & type in these keyword tags: Collaterals, experience, technology, events, publishing

Personal **Branding** Thumb-rule #19

## Praise publicly, Punish privately.

*How important is this thumb-rule to you?* ☆ ☆ ☆ ☆ ☆

*How will you improve your practice with this thumb-rule? Affirm it here.*

---

---

---

---

ACTION ITEMS:

---

---

*How well do you practice this thumb-rule?* low 1 2 3 4 5 6 high

For explanations, anecdotes, and book recommendations, go to *MarketingThumbrules.com* & type in these keyword tags: Controls, leadership, people, delegation, relationships

Personal **Branding** Thumb–rule #20

## Write out testimonial anecdotes for your clients & colleagues to sign.

*How important is this thumb-rule to you?* ☆ ☆ ☆ ☆ ☆

*How have other colleagues showcased this thumb-rule? Write it below:*

ACTION ITEMS:

*How well do you practice this thumb-rule?* low 1 2 3 4 5 6 high

For explanations, anecdotes, and book recommendations, go to *MarketingThumbrules.com* & type in these keyword tags: Collaterals, Community, relationships, reputation

Personal **Branding** Thumb-rule #21

---

## Leaders are readers.
## (They tend to play golf too.)

---

*How important is this thumb-rule to you?* ☆ ☆ ☆ ☆ ☆

*How will you improve your practice with this thumb-rule? Affirm it here:*

-----------------------------------------------------------------

-----------------------------------------------------------------

-----------------------------------------------------------------

-----------------------------------------------------------------

ACTION ITEMS:

-----------------------------------------------------------------

-----------------------------------------------------------------

*How well do you practice this thumb-rule?* low 1 2 3 4 5 6 high

For explanations, anecdotes, and book recommendations,
go to *MarketingThumbrules.com* & type in these keyword tags:
Competency, Community, experience, mindset

Personal **Branding** Thumb-rule #22

# Admit. Apologize.
# Ask for forgiveness. Amend quickly.

*How important is this thumb-rule to you?* ☆ ☆ ☆ ☆ ☆

*How have other colleagues showcased this thumb-rule? Write it below:*

------------------------------------------------------------

------------------------------------------------------------

------------------------------------------------------------

------------------------------------------------------------

ACTION ITEMS:

------------------------------------------------------------

------------------------------------------------------------

*How well do you practice this thumb-rule?* low 1 2 3 4 5 6 high

For explanations, anecdotes, and book recommendations,
go to *MarketingThumbrules.com* & type in these keyword tags:
Controls, leadership, relationships

Personal **Branding** Thumb-rule #23

> # Work your strengths.
> # Leverage other people's strengths.

*How important is this thumb-rule to you?* ☆ ☆ ☆ ☆ ☆

*How will you improve your practice with this thumb-rule? Affirm it here.*

-------------------------------------------------------------------

-------------------------------------------------------------------

-------------------------------------------------------------------

-------------------------------------------------------------------

ACTION ITEMS:

-------------------------------------------------------------------

-------------------------------------------------------------------

*How well do you practice this thumb-rule?* low 1  2  3  4  5  6  high

For explanations, anecdotes, and book recommendations,
go to *MarketingThumbrules.com* & type in these keyword tags:
Community, leadership, people, relationships

Personal **Branding** Thumb-rule #24

> # Widen your eyes. Lilt your voice.
> # Firm your handshake. Smile.

*How important is this thumb-rule to you?* ☆ ☆ ☆ ☆ ☆

*How have other colleagues showcased this thumb-rule? Write it below:*

......................................................................................

......................................................................................

......................................................................................

......................................................................................

......................................................................................

ACTION ITEMS:

......................................................................................

......................................................................................

*How well do you practice this thumb-rule?* low 1  2  3  4  5  6  high

For explanations, anecdotes, and book recommendations,
go to *MarketingThumbrules.com* & type in these keyword tags:
Charisma, relationships, people, smile

Personal **Branding** Thumb-rule #25

# Send informative e-newsletters.

*How important is this thumb-rule to you?* ☆ ☆ ☆ ☆ ☆

*How will you improve your practice with this thumb-rule? Affirm it here:*

ACTION ITEMS:

*How well do you practice this thumb-rule?* low 1 2 3 4 5 6 high

For explanations, anecdotes, and book recommendations, go to *MarketingThumbrules.com* & type in these keyword tags: Channels, Collaterals, Competency, relationships

Personal **Branding** Thumb-rule #26

# Join committees and volunteer to lead initiatives.

*How important is this thumb-rule to you?* ☆ ☆ ☆ ☆ ☆

*How have other colleagues showcased this thumb-rule? Write it below:*

_____

_____

_____

_____

ACTION ITEMS:

_____

_____

*How well do you practice this thumb-rule?* low 1 2 3 4 5 6 high

For explanations, anecdotes, and book recommendations, go to *MarketingThumbrules.com* & type in these keyword tags: Character, leadership, reputation

Personal **Branding** Thumb–rule #27

## Digitally audio record all of your seminars.

*How important is this thumb-rule to you?* ☆ ☆ ☆ ☆ ☆

*How will you improve your practice with this thumb-rule? Affirm it here.*

ACTION ITEMS:

*How well do you practice this thumb-rule?* low 1 2 3 4 5 6 high

For explanations, anecdotes, and book recommendations,
go to *MarketingThumbrules.com* & type in these keyword tags:
Collaterals, publishing, wealth, events

Personal **Branding** Thumb–rule #28

## Re-mind yourself everyday of your dreams, vision, goals, and habits.

*How important is this thumb-rule to you?* ☆ ☆ ☆ ☆ ☆

*How have other colleagues showcased this thumb-rule? Write it below:*

........................................................................................

........................................................................................

........................................................................................

........................................................................................

ACTION ITEMS:

........................................................................................

........................................................................................

*How well do you practice this thumb-rule?* low 1 2 3 4 5 6 high

For explanations, anecdotes, and book recommendations, go to *MarketingThumbrules.com* & type in these keyword tags: Charisma, Consistency, mindset, goals, vision

Personal **Branding** Thumb-rule #29

## Make people feel good.

*How important is this thumb-rule to you?* ☆ ☆ ☆ ☆ ☆

*How will you improve your practice with this thumb-rule? Affirm it here.*

ACTION ITEMS:

*How well do you practice this thumb-rule?* low 1 2 3 4 5 6 high

For explanations, anecdotes, and book recommendations, go to *MarketingThumbrules.com* & type in these keyword tags: Charisma, people, relationships

Personal **Branding** Thumb–rule #30

---

**Your special typeface, unique geometric elements, and colors – used consistently – are more important than artistic logos.**

---

*How important is this thumb-rule to you?* ☆ ☆ ☆ ☆ ☆

*How have other colleagues showcased this thumb-rule? Write it below:*

ACTION ITEMS:

*How well do you practice this thumb-rule?* low 1 2 3 4 5 6 high

For explanations, anecdotes, and book recommendations, go to *MarketingThumbrules.com* & type in these keyword tags: Collaterals, Consistency, message, publishing, technology

Personal **Branding** Thumb-rule #31

## Charismatic leaders are emotional, exaggerated, and eccentric as they envision an extraordinary future.

*How important is this thumb-rule to you?* ☆ ☆ ☆ ☆ ☆

*How will you improve your practice with this thumb-rule? Affirm it here.*

ACTION ITEMS:

*How well do you practice this thumb-rule?* low 1 2 3 4 5 6 high

For explanations, anecdotes, and book recommendations, go to *MarketingThumbrules.com* & type in these keyword tags: Charisma, leadership, experience, vision

Personal **Branding** Thumb-rule #32

## Edify others so they edify you.

*How important is this thumb-rule to you?* ☆ ☆ ☆ ☆ ☆

*How have other colleagues showcased this thumb-rule? Write it below:*

ACTION ITEMS:

*How well do you practice this thumb-rule?* low 1 2 3 4 5 6 high

For explanations, anecdotes, and book recommendations,
go to *MarketingThumbrules.com* & type in these keyword tags:
Character, Charisma, relationships

Personal **Branding** Thumb-rule #33

# Share anecdotes of your achievements.

*How important is this thumb-rule to you?* ☆ ☆ ☆ ☆ ☆

*How will you improve your practice with this thumb-rule? Affirm it here.*

ACTION ITEMS:

*How well do you practice this thumb-rule?* low  1  2  3  4  5  6  high

For explanations, anecdotes, and book recommendations, go to *MarketingThumbrules.com* & type in these keyword tags: Collaterals, experience, results

Personal **Branding** Thumb-rule #34

> # Prepare, to think on your feet.

*How important is this thumb-rule to you?* ☆ ☆ ☆ ☆ ☆

*How have other colleagues showcased this thumb-rule? Write it below:*

---

---

---

---

---

ACTION ITEMS:

---

---

*How well do you practice this thumb-rule?* low 1 2 3 4 5 6 high

For explanations, anecdotes, and book recommendations, go to *MarketingThumbrules.com* & type in these keyword tags: Competency, Controls, experience, events

Personal **Branding** Thumb-rule #35

# A standard newspaper column is 800 words long.

*How important is this thumb-rule to you?* ☆ ☆ ☆ ☆ ☆

*How will you improve your practice with this thumb-rule? Affirm it here.*

ACTION ITEMS:

*How well do you practice this thumb-rule?* low 1 2 3 4 5 6 high

For explanations, anecdotes, and book recommendations, go to *MarketingThumbrules.com* & type in these keyword tags: Collaterals, publishing

Personal **Branding** Thumb-rule #36

## Give talkative, gregarious (influential) people something positive to say about you.

*How important is this thumb-rule to you?* ☆ ☆ ☆ ☆ ☆

*How have other colleagues showcased this thumb-rule? Write it below:*

ACTION ITEMS:

*How well do you practice this thumb-rule?* low 1 2 3 4 5 6 high

For explanations, anecdotes, and book recommendations, go to *MarketingThumbrules.com* & type in these keyword tags: Collaterals, catchphrase, people

Personal **Branding** Thumb-rule #37

# Give credit when you borrow ideas and quote others.

*How important is this thumb-rule to you?* ☆ ☆ ☆ ☆ ☆

*How will you improve your practice with this thumb-rule? Affirm it here.*

ACTION ITEMS:

*How well do you practice this thumb-rule?* low  1  2  3  4  5  6  high

For explanations, anecdotes, and book recommendations, go to *MarketingThumbrules.com* & type in these keyword tags: Character, Collaterals, people, publishing

Personal **Branding** Thumb-rule #38

# Copy why you belong to fan clubs & prefer certain brands (communities).

*How important is this thumb-rule to you?* ☆ ☆ ☆ ☆ ☆

*How have other colleagues showcased this thumb-rule? Write it below:*

ACTION ITEMS:

*How well do you practice this thumb-rule?* low 1 2 3 4 5 6 high

For explanations, anecdotes, and book recommendations, go to *MarketingThumbrules.com* & type in these keyword tags: Community, experience

Personal **Branding** Thumb–rule #39

## Always carry breath mints.

*How important is this thumb-rule to you?* ☆ ☆ ☆ ☆ ☆

*How will you improve your practice with this thumb-rule? Affirm it here:*

ACTION ITEMS:

*How well do you practice this thumb-rule?* low 1 2 3 4 5 6 high

For explanations, anecdotes, and book recommendations, go to *MarketingThumbrules.com* & type in these keyword tags: Character, networking, relationships

Personal **Branding** Thumb–rule #40

## Work with a coach to get out of your own way.

How important is this thumb-rule to you? ☆ ☆ ☆ ☆ ☆

How have other colleagues showcased this thumb-rule? Write it below:

___

___

___

___

ACTION ITEMS:

___

___

How well do you practice this thumb-rule? low 1 2 3 4 5 6 high

For explanations, anecdotes, and book recommendations, go to *MarketingThumbrules.com* & type in these keyword tags: Charisma, people, results

Personal **Branding** Thumb–rule #41

> **HANDSHAKE ETIQUETTE:**
> **Firm, not crushing; never wimpy.**
> **1 to 2 seconds; don't over-shake.**
> **Please don't be wet or clammy.**

*How important is this thumb-rule to you?* ☆ ☆ ☆ ☆ ☆

*How will you improve your practice with this thumb-rule? Affirm it here.*

ACTION ITEMS:

*How well do you practice this thumb-rule?* low 1 2 3 4 5 6 high

For explanations, anecdotes, and book recommendations,
go to *MarketingThumbrules.com* & type in these keyword tags:
Character, people, relationships

Personal **Branding** Thumb-rule #42

## People trust, enjoy, and prefer what is familiar.

*How important is this thumb-rule to you?* ☆ ☆ ☆ ☆ ☆

*How have other colleagues showcased this thumb-rule? Write it below:*

ACTION ITEMS:

*How well do you practice this thumb-rule?* low 1 2 3 4 5 6 high

For explanations, anecdotes, and book recommendations, go to *MarketingThumbrules.com* & type in these keyword tags: Consistency, Community, Collaterals, people, experience, system

Personal **Branding** Thumb–rule #43

> # Show-off the letters after your name.

*How important is this thumb-rule to you?* ☆ ☆ ☆ ☆ ☆

*How will you improve your practice with this thumb-rule? Affirm it here.*

ACTION ITEMS:

*How well do you practice this thumb-rule?* low 1   2   3   4   5   6   high

For explanations, anecdotes, and book recommendations,
go to *MarketingThumbrules.com* & type in these keyword tags:
Competency, experience

Personal **Branding** Thumb-rule #44

> # How many others have your certifications? Showcase something more distinctive about you.

*How important is this thumb-rule to you?* ☆ ☆ ☆ ☆ ☆

*How have other colleagues showcased this thumb-rule? Write it below:*

ACTION ITEMS:

*How well do you practice this thumb-rule?* low 1 2 3 4 5 6 high

For explanations, anecdotes, and book recommendations, go to *MarketingThumbrules.com* & type in these keyword tags: Character, Collaterals, experience, message, questions

Personal **Branding** Thumb-rule #45

## Get paid for marketing yourself by selling knowledge products.

*How important is this thumb-rule to you?* ☆ ☆ ☆ ☆ ☆

*How will you improve your practice with this thumb-rule? Affirm it here.*

ACTION ITEMS:

*How well do you practice this thumb-rule?* low 1 2 3 4 5 6 high

For explanations, anecdotes, and book recommendations, go to *MarketingThumbrules.com* & type in these keyword tags: Collaterals, Competency, publishing, wealth

Personal **Branding** Thumb–rule #46

## Be passionate.

*How important is this thumb-rule to you?* ☆ ☆ ☆ ☆ ☆

*How have other colleagues showcased this thumb-rule? Write it below:*

ACTION ITEMS:

*How well do you practice this thumb-rule?* low 1  2  3  4  5  6  high

For explanations, anecdotes, and book recommendations, go to *MarketingThumbrules.com* & type in these keyword tags: Charisma, leadership, relationships

Personal **Branding** Thumb-rule #47

# Buy lunch for your Compliance Officer. Is that ethical?

*How important is this thumb-rule to you?* ☆ ☆ ☆ ☆ ☆

*How will you improve your practice with this thumb-rule? Affirm it here.*

ACTION ITEMS:

*How well do you practice this thumb-rule?* low 1  2  3  4  5  6  high

For explanations, anecdotes, and book recommendations, go to *MarketingThumbrules.com* & type in these keyword tags:
Controls, Character, people, relationships, compliance, questions

Personal **Branding** Thumb–rule #48

> # Belong to very few networking groups, and be very active in them.

*How important is this thumb-rule to you?* ☆ ☆ ☆ ☆ ☆

*How have other colleagues showcased this thumb-rule? Write it below:*

ACTION ITEMS:

*How well do you practice this thumb-rule?* low 1 2 3 4 5 6 high

For explanations, anecdotes, and book recommendations, go to *MarketingThumbrules.com* & type in these keyword tags: Channels, networking, relationships

Personal **Branding** Thumb-rule #49

> # Ask journalists what they're working on: Offer your help (and quotes).

*How important is this thumb-rule to you?*  ☆ ☆ ☆ ☆ ☆

*How will you improve your practice with this thumb-rule? Affirm it here.*

---

---

---

---

ACTION ITEMS:

---

---

*How well do you practice this thumb-rule?* low  1  2  3  4  5  6  high

For explanations, anecdotes, and book recommendations, go to *MarketingThumbrules.com* & type in these keyword tags: Channels, relationships, publishing, questions

Personal **Branding** Thumb–rule #50

# Become friends with leaders.
# 'Who to know' now knows you.

*How important is this thumb-rule to you?* ☆ ☆ ☆ ☆ ☆

*How have other colleagues showcased this thumb-rule? Write it below:*

---

---

---

---

ACTION ITEMS:

---

---

*How well do you practice this thumb-rule?* low 1 2 3 4 5 6 high

For explanations, anecdotes, and book recommendations, go to *MarketingThumbrules.com* & type in these keyword tags: Character, relationships, reputation

Personal **Branding** Thumb–rule #51

## Listen to how people introduce you to their colleagues. How far off are they? It's your fault.

*How important is this thumb-rule to you?* ☆ ☆ ☆ ☆ ☆

*How will you improve your practice with this thumb-rule? Affirm it here.*

ACTION ITEMS:

*How well do you practice this thumb-rule?* low 1 2 3 4 5 6 high

For explanations, anecdotes, and book recommendations, go to *MarketingThumbrules.com* & type in these keyword tags: Character, catchphrase, message, networking, questions

Personal **Branding** Thumb–rule #52

## Who are the professionals you admire? Cut and paste a role model collage.

*How important is this thumb-rule to you?* ☆ ☆ ☆ ☆ ☆

*How have other colleagues showcased this thumb-rule? Write it below:*

ACTION ITEMS:

*How well do you practice this thumb-rule?* low 1 2 3 4 5 6 high

For explanations, anecdotes, and book recommendations,
go to *MarketingThumbrules.com* & type in these keyword tags:
Character, Charisma, people, vision, values, mindset, questions

Personal **Branding** Thumb-rule #53

## Popularize "The 'Remember-Me' Guy" nickname for yourself.

*How important is this thumb-rule to you?* ☆ ☆ ☆ ☆ ☆

*How will you improve your practice with this thumb-rule? Affirm it here.*

---

---

---

---

ACTION ITEMS:

---

---

*How well do you practice this thumb-rule?* low 1 2 3 4 5 6 high

For explanations, anecdotes, and book recommendations, go to *MarketingThumbrules.com* & type in these keyword tags: Character, catchphrase, networking, message, experience

Personal **Branding** Thumb–rule #54

> # A mascot can be your best friend:
> ## Animate your ideal customer, worst customer, best employee, worst competitor, or your personal brand.

How important is this thumb-rule to you? ☆ ☆ ☆ ☆ ☆

How have other colleagues showcased this thumb-rule? Write it below:

..........................................................................................................

..........................................................................................................

..........................................................................................................

..........................................................................................................

ACTION ITEMS:

..........................................................................................................

..........................................................................................................

How well do you practice this thumb-rule? low 1 2 3 4 5 6 high

For explanations, anecdotes, and book recommendations, go to *MarketingThumbrules.com* & type in these keyword tags: Character, Collaterals, people, message

Personal **Branding** Thumb-rule #55

# Get over it. Don't take it personally.

*How important is this thumb-rule to you?* ☆ ☆ ☆ ☆ ☆

*How will you improve your practice with this thumb-rule? Affirm it here.*

ACTION ITEMS:

*How well do you practice this thumb-rule?* low 1 2 3 4 5 6 high

For explanations, anecdotes, and book recommendations,
go to *MarketingThumbrules.com* & type in these keyword tags:
Character, leadership, mindset, smile

Personal **Branding** Thumb-rule #56

# Never underestimate the power of novelty or controversy.

How important is this thumb-rule to you? ☆ ☆ ☆ ☆ ☆

How have other colleagues showcased this thumb-rule? Write it below:

ACTION ITEMS:

How well do you practice this thumb-rule? low 1 2 3 4 5 6 high

For explanations, anecdotes, and book recommendations, go to *MarketingThumbrules.com* & type in these keyword tags: Currency, Community, message

Personal **Branding** Thumb–rule #57

# We're all selling hope through our confidence.

*How important is this thumb-rule to you?* ☆ ☆ ☆ ☆ ☆

*How will you improve your practice with this thumb-rule? Affirm it here:*

---

---

---

---

ACTION ITEMS:

---

---

*How well do you practice this thumb-rule?* low 1 2 3 4 5 6 high

For explanations, anecdotes, and book recommendations, go to *MarketingThumbrules.com* & type in these keyword tags: Charisma, experience, reputation

Personal **Branding** Thumb-rule #58

## Link to your earlier blog posts on your recent posts & comments.

*How important is this thumb-rule to you?* ☆ ☆ ☆ ☆ ☆

*How have other colleagues showcased this thumb-rule? Write it below:*

ACTION ITEMS:

*How well do you practice this thumb-rule?* low 1 2 3 4 5 6 high

For explanations, anecdotes, and book recommendations, go to *MarketingThumbrules.com* & type in these keyword tags: Collaterals, Consistency, technology

Personal **Branding** Thumb-rule #59

## Update your fashion style.
## Look like your own brand of success.

*How important is this thumb-rule to you?* ☆ ☆ ☆ ☆ ☆

*How will you improve your practice with this thumb-rule? Affirm it here.*

---

---

---

---

ACTION ITEMS:

---

---

*How well do you practice this thumb-rule?* low 1 2 3 4 5 6 high

For explanations, anecdotes, and book recommendations, go to *MarketingThumbrules.com* & type in these keyword tags: Character, style

Personal **Branding** Thumb-rule #60

## Don't interrupt meetings with your cell phone or gadgetry.

How important is this thumb-rule to you? ☆ ☆ ☆ ☆ ☆

How have other colleagues showcased this thumb-rule? Write it below:

ACTION ITEMS:

How well do you practice this thumb-rule? low 1 2 3 4 5 6 high

For explanations, anecdotes, and book recommendations, go to *MarketingThumbrules.com* & type in these keyword tags: Character, relationships, experience, technology

Personal **Branding** Thumb–rule #61

## Talk about your role models.

*How important is this thumb-rule to you?* ☆ ☆ ☆ ☆ ☆

*How will you improve your practice with this thumb-rule? Affirm it here.*

ACTION ITEMS:

*How well do you practice this thumb-rule?* low 1  2  3  4  5  6  high

For explanations, anecdotes, and book recommendations,
go to *MarketingThumbrules.com* & type in these keyword tags:
Character, leadership, people, delegation, reputation, values

Personal **Branding** Thumb-rule #62

**Empower your spiritual charisma:
Pray & meditate.**

How important is this thumb-rule to you? ☆ ☆ ☆ ☆ ☆

How have other colleagues showcased this thumb-rule? Write it below:

ACTION ITEMS:

How well do you practice this thumb-rule? low 1 2 3 4 5 6 high

For explanations, anecdotes, and book recommendations,
go to *MarketingThumbrules.com* & type in these keyword tags:
Charisma, values, mindset

Personal **Branding** Thumb-rule #63

---

# Decorate your office with memorabilia. Carry around memorable conversation pieces.

---

*How important is this thumb-rule to you?* ☆ ☆ ☆ ☆ ☆

*How will you improve your practice with this thumb-rule? Affirm it here.*

ACTION ITEMS:

*How well do you practice this thumb-rule?* low 1 2 3 4 5 6 high

For explanations, anecdotes, and book recommendations, go to *MarketingThumbrules.com* & type in these keyword tags: Character, Collaterals, experience, networking

Personal **Branding** Thumb–rule #64

# The grass isn't greener since your shadow follows you.

*How important is this thumb-rule to you?* ☆ ☆ ☆ ☆ ☆

*How have other colleagues showcased this thumb-rule? Write it below:*

ACTION ITEMS:

*How well do you practice this thumb-rule?* low 1 2 3 4 5 6 high

For explanations, anecdotes, and book recommendations, go to *MarketingThumbrules.com* & type in these keyword tags: Character, Charisma, mindset, values

Personal **Branding** Thumb–rule #65

## Don't get wasted with clients & colleagues.

*How important is this thumb-rule to you?* ☆ ☆ ☆ ☆ ☆

*How will you improve your practice with this thumb-rule? Affirm it here.*

ACTION ITEMS:

*How well do you practice this thumb-rule?* low 1 2 3 4 5 6 high

For explanations, anecdotes, and book recommendations, go to *MarketingThumbrules.com* & type in these keyword tags: Character, reputation, values

Personal **Branding** Thumb-rule #66

# Write articles for your colleagues' newsletters.

*How important is this thumb-rule to you?* ☆ ☆ ☆ ☆ ☆

*How have other colleagues showcased this thumb-rule? Write it below:*

ACTION ITEMS:

*How well do you practice this thumb-rule?* low 1 2 3 4 5 6 high

For explanations, anecdotes, and book recommendations, go to *MarketingThumbrules.com* & type in these keyword tags: Collaterals, relationships, publishing

Personal **Branding** Thumb-rule #67

## Coin your own phrase, acronym, jargon, spelling, or definition to brand common language.

*How important is this thumb-rule to you?* ☆ ☆ ☆ ☆ ☆

*How will you improve your practice with this thumb-rule? Affirm it here.*

ACTION ITEMS:

*How well do you practice this thumb-rule?* low 1　2　3　4　5　6　high

For explanations, anecdotes, and book recommendations, go to *MarketingThumbrules.com* & type in these keyword tags: Collaterals, catchphrase, message, wealth, compliance

Personal **Branding** Thumb-rule #68

# Your headshot should show-off your personality.

*How important is this thumb-rule to you?* ☆ ☆ ☆ ☆ ☆

*How have other colleagues showcased this thumb-rule? Write it below:*

ACTION ITEMS:

*How well do you practice this thumb-rule?* low 1  2  3  4  5  6  high

For explanations, anecdotes, and book recommendations, go to *MarketingThumbrules.com* & type in these keyword tags: Character, Collaterals

Personal **Branding** Thumb-rule #69

## Be polite. It's charming.

*How important is this thumb-rule to you?* ☆ ☆ ☆ ☆ ☆

*How will you improve your practice with this thumb-rule? Affirm it here.*

ACTION ITEMS:

*How well do you practice this thumb-rule?* low 1  2  3  4  5  6  high

For explanations, anecdotes, and book recommendations, go to *MarketingThumbrules.com* & type in these keyword tags: Charisma, people, relationships

Personal **Branding** Thumb-rule #70

# Spell people's names correctly... especially if it's unfamiliar to you.

*How important is this thumb-rule to you?* ☆ ☆ ☆ ☆ ☆

*How have other colleagues showcased this thumb-rule? Write it below:*

ACTION ITEMS:

*How well do you practice this thumb-rule?* low 1 2 3 4 5 6 high

For explanations, anecdotes, and book recommendations, go to *MarketingThumbrules.com* & type in these keyword tags: Character, relationships

Personal **Branding** Thumb–rule #71

## Say people's names correctly, or gently ask, "Am I pronouncing your name right?" Never make a joke!

*How important is this thumb-rule to you?* ☆ ☆ ☆ ☆ ☆

*How will you improve your practice with this thumb-rule? Affirm it here.*

ACTION ITEMS:

*How well do you practice this thumb-rule?* low 1 2 3 4 5 6 high

For explanations, anecdotes, and book recommendations, go to *MarketingThumbrules.com* & type in these keyword tags: Character, relationships, questions

Personal **Branding** Thumb-rule #72

## Practice sincerely thanking when receiving a compliment: Don't be too self-deprecating, shy, arrogant, or complacent.

*How important is this thumb-rule to you?* ☆ ☆ ☆ ☆ ☆

*How have other colleagues showcased this thumb-rule? Write it below:*

ACTION ITEMS:

*How well do you practice this thumb-rule?* low 1 2 3 4 5 6 high

For explanations, anecdotes, and book recommendations, go to *MarketingThumbrules.com* & type in these keyword tags: Character, Charisma, relationships, networking, smile

Personal **Branding** Thumb-rule #73

## Practice complimenting others with a sincere smile and eye contact.

*How important is this thumb-rule to you?* ☆ ☆ ☆ ☆ ☆

*How will you improve your practice with this thumb-rule? Affirm it here.*

ACTION ITEMS:

*How well do you practice this thumb-rule?* low 1 2 3 4 5 6 high

For explanations, anecdotes, and book recommendations, go to *MarketingThumbrules.com* & type in these keyword tags: Charisma, smile, relationships

Personal **Branding** Thumb-rule #74

> # ur grammr & spllng r imprtnt.

*How important is this thumb-rule to you?* ☆ ☆ ☆ ☆ ☆

*How have other colleagues showcased this thumb-rule? Write it below:*

ACTION ITEMS:

*How well do you practice this thumb-rule?* low 1 2 3 4 5 6 high

For explanations, anecdotes, and book recommendations, go to *MarketingThumbrules.com* & type in these keyword tags: Character, Collaterals, publishing

Personal **Branding** Thumb–rule #75

> # Learn knowledge. Collect knowledge. Distribute knowledge. Nowadays: Create knowledge.

*How important is this thumb-rule to you?* ☆ ☆ ☆ ☆ ☆

*How will you improve your practice with this thumb-rule? Affirm it here.*

ACTION ITEMS:

*How well do you practice this thumb-rule?* low 1 2 3 4 5 6 high

For explanations, anecdotes, and book recommendations, go to *MarketingThumbrules.com* & type in these keyword tags: Competency, publishing

Personal **Branding** Thumb-rule #76

---

**RHYTHM, CRESCENDO, TIMING:**
**Sing along & dance to your**
**favorite music before you present.**

---

*How important is this thumb-rule to you?* ☆ ☆ ☆ ☆ ☆

*How have other colleagues showcased this thumb-rule? Write it below:*

.......................................................................................................

.......................................................................................................

.......................................................................................................

.......................................................................................................

.......................................................................................................

ACTION ITEMS:

.......................................................................................................

.......................................................................................................

*How well do you practice this thumb-rule?* low 1  2  3  4  5  6  high

For explanations, anecdotes, and book recommendations,
go to *MarketingThumbrules.com* & type in these keyword tags:
Character, Charisma, smile, experience, mindset, presentation

Personal **Branding** Thumb–rule #77

# Make eye contact around the room when you present.

*How important is this thumb-rule to you?* ☆ ☆ ☆ ☆ ☆

*How will you improve your practice with this thumb-rule? Affirm it here.*

ACTION ITEMS:

*How well do you practice this thumb-rule?* low 1 2 3 4 5 6 high

For explanations, anecdotes, and book recommendations, go to *MarketingThumbrules.com* & type in these keyword tags: Charisma, networking, events

Personal **Branding** Thumb-rule #78

## Memorize your opening words to grab attention, like a cue ball breaker.

*How important is this thumb-rule to you?* ☆ ☆ ☆ ☆ ☆

*How have other colleagues showcased this thumb-rule? Write it below:*

ACTION ITEMS:

*How well do you practice this thumb-rule?* low 1 2 3 4 5 6 high

For explanations, anecdotes, and book recommendations, go to *MarketingThumbrules.com* & type in these keyword tags: Collaterals, message, presentation, experience, events

Personal **Branding** Thumb-rule #79

## For your memory notes:
## Jot bullet points, not full sentences.

*How important is this thumb-rule to you?* ☆ ☆ ☆ ☆ ☆

*How will you improve your practice with this thumb-rule? Affirm it here.*

ACTION ITEMS:

*How well do you practice this thumb-rule?* low 1 2 3 4 5 6 high

For explanations, anecdotes, and book recommendations,
go to *MarketingThumbrules.com* & type in these keyword tags:
Collaterals, message, presentation, experience, events

Personal **Branding** Thumb-rule #80

## It's all about the photo op!

*How important is this thumb-rule to you?* ☆ ☆ ☆ ☆ ☆

*How have other colleagues showcased this thumb-rule? Write it below:*

ACTION ITEMS:

*How well do you practice this thumb-rule?* low 1 2 3 4 5 6 high

For explanations, anecdotes, and book recommendations,
go to *MarketingThumbrules.com* & type in these keyword tags:
Character, Collaterals, style, presentation

Personal **Branding** Thumb–rule #81

---

# If your picture isn't attractive or distinctive, leave it off!

---

*How important is this thumb-rule to you?* ☆ ☆ ☆ ☆ ☆

*How will you improve your practice with this thumb-rule? Affirm it here.*

ACTION ITEMS:

*How well do you practice this thumb-rule?* low 1 2 3 4 5 6 high

For explanations, anecdotes, and book recommendations, go to *MarketingThumbrules.com* & type in these keyword tags: Collaterals, Character, presentation

Personal **Branding** Thumb-rule #82

## Learn enough about current events, pop culture, & industry news to chat. Don't become a newsaholic.

*How important is this thumb-rule to you?* ☆ ☆ ☆ ☆ ☆

*How have other colleagues showcased this thumb-rule? Write it below:*

ACTION ITEMS:

*How well do you practice this thumb-rule?* low 1 2 3 4 5 6 high

For explanations, anecdotes, and book recommendations, go to *MarketingThumbrules.com* & type in these keyword tags: Competency, networking, relationships

Personal **Branding** Thumb–rule #83

## Nominate yourself for awards.

*How important is this thumb-rule to you?* ☆ ☆ ☆ ☆ ☆

*How will you improve your practice with this thumb-rule? Affirm it here.*

ACTION ITEMS:

*How well do you practice this thumb-rule?* low 1 2 3 4 5 6 high

For explanations, anecdotes, and book recommendations, go to *MarketingThumbrules.com* & type in these keyword tags: Collaterals, recognition

Personal **Branding** Thumb–rule #84

## Don't wear your suit jacket while driving; it wrinkles easily. Hang it off the back hook.

*How important is this thumb-rule to you?*  ☆ ☆ ☆ ☆ ☆

*How have other colleagues showcased this thumb-rule? Write it below:*

ACTION ITEMS:

*How well do you practice this thumb-rule?*  low  1  2  3  4  5  6  high

For explanations, anecdotes, and book recommendations, go to *MarketingThumbrules.com* & type in these keyword tags: Character, style, presentation

Personal **Branding** Thumb–rule #85

## Everybody represents at least 250 relationships.

*How important is this thumb-rule to you?* ☆ ☆ ☆ ☆ ☆

*How will you improve your practice with this thumb-rule? Affirm it here.*

ACTION ITEMS:

*How well do you practice this thumb-rule?* low 1 2 3 4 5 6 high

For explanations, anecdotes, and book recommendations, go to *MarketingThumbrules.com* & type in these keyword tags: Community, networking, relationships

Personal **Branding** Thumb-rule #86

# Nothing is off the record.
# ...Especially on-line.

How important is this thumb-rule to you? ☆ ☆ ☆ ☆ ☆

How have other colleagues showcased this thumb-rule? Write it below:

ACTION ITEMS:

How well do you practice this thumb-rule? low 1 2 3 4 5 6 high

For explanations, anecdotes, and book recommendations,
go to *MarketingThumbrules.com* & type in these keyword tags:
Character, reputation, publishing

Professional **Prospecting** Thumb–rule #1

## Measure activities, not just results.

*How important is this thumb-rule to you?* ☆ ☆ ☆ ☆ ☆

*What kind of habits does this thumb-rule inspire for you? Write it below:*

.........................................................................................................

.........................................................................................................

.........................................................................................................

.........................................................................................................

ACTION ITEMS:

.........................................................................................................

.........................................................................................................

*How well do you practice this thumb-rule?* low 1 2 3 4 5 6 high

For explanations, anecdotes, and book recommendations,
go to *MarketingThumbrules.com* & type in these keyword tags:
Controls, goals

Professional **Prospecting** Thumb-rule #2

> # Encourage in-links and improve your meta tags to increase your web search results page rank.

*How important is this thumb-rule to you?* ☆ ☆ ☆ ☆ ☆

*How many different ways can you use this thumb-rule? Share it here:*

---

---

---

---

ACTION ITEMS:

---

---

*How well do you practice this thumb-rule?* low 1 2 3 4 5 6 high

For explanations, anecdotes, and book recommendations, go to *MarketingThumbrules.com* & type in these keyword tags: Channels, technology

Professional **Prospecting** Thumb–rule #3

# Weekly Planning is fundamental to working strategically.

*How important is this thumb-rule to you?* ☆ ☆ ☆ ☆ ☆

*What kind of habits does this thumb-rule inspire for you? Write it below:*

---

---

---

---

ACTION ITEMS:

---

---

*How well do you practice this thumb-rule?* low 1 2 3 4 5 6 high

For explanations, anecdotes, and book recommendations, go to *MarketingThumbrules.com* & type in these keyword tags: Controls, planning, goals, time, prioritize

Professional **Prospecting** Thumb-rule #4

> # Friendship first.
> # Business second.

*How important is this thumb-rule to you?* ☆ ☆ ☆ ☆ ☆

*How many different ways can you use this thumb-rule? Share it here:*

......................................................................................................................

......................................................................................................................

......................................................................................................................

......................................................................................................................

ACTION ITEMS:

......................................................................................................................

......................................................................................................................

*How well do you practice this thumb-rule?* low 1 2 3 4 5 6 high

For explanations, anecdotes, and book recommendations,
go to *MarketingThumbrules.com* & type in these keyword tags:
Character, relationships, mindset

Professional **Prospecting** Thumb–rule #5

# Don't use more than 3 fonts around each other.

*How important is this thumb-rule to you?* ☆ ☆ ☆ ☆ ☆

*What kind of habits does this thumb-rule inspire for you? Write it below:*

ACTION ITEMS:

*How well do you practice this thumb-rule?* low 1 2 3 4 5 6 high

For explanations, anecdotes, and book recommendations, go to *MarketingThumbrules.com* & type in these keyword tags: Collaterals, Consistency, presentation, publishing, technology

Professional **Prospecting** Thumb-rule #6

# Exploit buzzwords.

How important is this thumb-rule to you? ☆ ☆ ☆ ☆ ☆

How many different ways can you use this thumb-rule? Share it here:

ACTION ITEMS:

How well do you practice this thumb-rule? low 1 2 3 4 5 6 high

For explanations, anecdotes, and book recommendations, go to *MarketingThumbrules.com* & type in these keyword tags: Currency, message, presentation

Professional **Prospecting** Thumb–rule #7

---

# Converse about their hobbies, interests, and values.

---

*How important is this thumb-rule to you?* ☆ ☆ ☆ ☆ ☆

*What kind of habits does this thumb-rule inspire for you? Write it below:*

---

ACTION ITEMS:

---

*How well do you practice this thumb-rule?* low 1 2 3 4 5 6 high

For explanations, anecdotes, and book recommendations, go to *MarketingThumbrules.com* & type in these keyword tags: Character, relationships

Professional **Prospecting** Thumb-rule #8

# What you measure you can improve.

*How important is this thumb-rule to you?* ☆ ☆ ☆ ☆ ☆

*How many different ways can you use this thumb-rule? Share it here:*

ACTION ITEMS:

*How well do you practice this thumb-rule?* low 1 2 3 4 5 6 high

For explanations, anecdotes, and book recommendations, go to *MarketingThumbrules.com* & type in these keyword tags: Controls, goals, results

Professional **Prospecting** Thumb-rule #9

## Build in incentives to encourage word-of-mouth marketing.

*How important is this thumb-rule to you?* ☆ ☆ ☆ ☆ ☆

*What kind of habits does this thumb-rule inspire for you? Write it below:*

ACTION ITEMS:

*How well do you practice this thumb-rule?* low  1  2  3  4  5  6  high

For explanations, anecdotes, and book recommendations, go to *MarketingThumbrules.com* & type in these keyword tags: Channels, networking, affiliates

Professional **Prospecting** Thumb-rule #10

## Dedicate at least 20% of your productive time to marketing.

How important is this thumb-rule to you? ☆ ☆ ☆ ☆ ☆

*How many different ways can you use this thumb-rule? Share it here:*

ACTION ITEMS:

*How well do you practice this thumb-rule?* low 1 2 3 4 5 6 high

For explanations, anecdotes, and book recommendations, go to *MarketingThumbrules.com* & type in these keyword tags: Controls, time, prioritize

Professional **Prospecting** Thumb–rule #11

---

# Hitch upon a star:
# Name anyone or anything popular.

---

*How important is this thumb-rule to you?* ☆ ☆ ☆ ☆ ☆

*What kind of habits does this thumb-rule inspire for you? Write it below:*

---------------------------------------------------------------

---------------------------------------------------------------

---------------------------------------------------------------

---------------------------------------------------------------

ACTION ITEMS:

---------------------------------------------------------------

---------------------------------------------------------------

*How well do you practice this thumb-rule?* low 1  2  3  4  5  6  high

For explanations, anecdotes, and book recommendations,
go to *MarketingThumbrules.com* & type in these keyword tags:
Currency, presentation

Professional **Prospecting** Thumb-rule #12

> # If you keep doing what you're doing, you'll keep getting what you're getting.

*How important is this thumb-rule to you?* ☆ ☆ ☆ ☆ ☆

*How many different ways can you use this thumb-rule? Share it here:*

---

---

---

---

ACTION ITEMS:

---

---

*How well do you practice this thumb-rule?* low 1 2 3 4 5 6 high

For explanations, anecdotes, and book recommendations, go to *MarketingThumbrules.com* & type in these keyword tags: Controls, goals, results

Professional **Prospecting** Thumb-rule #13

# Give out free stuff, with your contact info on it.

*How important is this thumb-rule to you?* ☆ ☆ ☆ ☆ ☆

*What kind of habits does this thumb-rule inspire for you? Write it below:*

ACTION ITEMS:

*How well do you practice this thumb-rule?* low 1  2  3  4  5  6  high

For explanations, anecdotes, and book recommendations, go to *MarketingThumbrules.com* & type in these keyword tags: Collaterals, relationships

Professional **Prospecting** Thumb-rule #14

> # Say what you're going to say, say it, then say what you've said.

*How important is this thumb-rule to you?* ☆ ☆ ☆ ☆ ☆

*How many different ways can you use this thumb-rule? Share it here:*

ACTION ITEMS:

*How well do you practice this thumb-rule?* low 1 2 3 4 5 6 high

For explanations, anecdotes, and book recommendations, go to *MarketingThumbrules.com* & type in these keyword tags: Character, message, presentation

Professional **Prospecting** Thumb-rule #15

## For better networking, go early and stay late.

*How important is this thumb-rule to you?* ☆ ☆ ☆ ☆ ☆

*What kind of habits does this thumb-rule inspire for you? Write it below:*

ACTION ITEMS:

*How well do you practice this thumb-rule?* low 1  2  3  4  5  6  high

For explanations, anecdotes, and book recommendations, go to *MarketingThumbrules.com* & type in these keyword tags: Channels, networking, relationships

Professional **Prospecting** Thumb-rule #16

## Fill your website with text your prospects, clients, and partners would search for.

*How important is this thumb-rule to you?* ☆ ☆ ☆ ☆ ☆

*How many different ways can you use this thumb-rule? Share it here:*

--------------------------------------------------

--------------------------------------------------

--------------------------------------------------

--------------------------------------------------

ACTION ITEMS:

--------------------------------------------------

--------------------------------------------------

*How well do you practice this thumb-rule?* low 1 2 3 4 5 6 high

For explanations, anecdotes, and book recommendations, go to *MarketingThumbrules.com* & type in these keyword tags: Collaterals, technology, message

Professional **Prospecting** Thumb–rule #17

## 1 out of 3 people will show up.

*How important is this thumb-rule to you?* ☆ ☆ ☆ ☆ ☆

*What kind of habits does this thumb-rule inspire for you? Write it below:*

ACTION ITEMS:

*How well do you practice this thumb-rule?* low 1 2 3 4 5 6 high

For explanations, anecdotes, and book recommendations, go to *MarketingThumbrules.com* & type in these keyword tags: Collaterals, presentation, networking, results

Professional **Prospecting** Thumb-rule #18

## Cold calling & cold mailing receives 1 response for every 100 deliveries.

*How important is this thumb-rule to you?* ☆ ☆ ☆ ☆ ☆

*How many different ways can you use this thumb-rule? Share it here:*

ACTION ITEMS:

*How well do you practice this thumb-rule?* low 1 2 3 4 5 6 high

For explanations, anecdotes, and book recommendations, go to *MarketingThumbrules.com* & type in these keyword tags: Channels, results

Professional **Prospecting** Thumb–rule #19

> # Most people veer to the right in any room (office, stores, tradeshows, seminars).

*How important is this thumb-rule to you?* ☆ ☆ ☆ ☆ ☆

*What kind of habits does this thumb-rule inspire for you? Write it below:*

---

---

---

---

ACTION ITEMS:

---

---

*How well do you practice this thumb-rule?* low 1 2 3 4 5 6 high

For explanations, anecdotes, and book recommendations, go to *MarketingThumbrules.com* & type in these keyword tags: Community, networking, people

Professional **Prospecting** Thumb-rule #20

## People keep magnets.

*How important is this thumb-rule to you?* ☆ ☆ ☆ ☆ ☆

*How many different ways can you use this thumb-rule? Share it here:*

ACTION ITEMS:

*How well do you practice this thumb-rule?* low  1  2  3  4  5  6  high

For explanations, anecdotes, and book recommendations, go to *MarketingThumbrules.com* & type in these keyword tags: Collaterals, people, message

Professional **Prospecting** Thumb–rule #21

# B.Y.O.B.
# Bring Your Own Badge.

*How important is this thumb-rule to you?* ☆ ☆ ☆ ☆ ☆

*What kind of habits does this thumb-rule inspire for you? Write it below:*

........................................................................................

........................................................................................

........................................................................................

........................................................................................

ACTION ITEMS:

........................................................................................

........................................................................................

*How well do you practice this thumb-rule?* low 1  2  3  4  5  6 high

For explanations, anecdotes, and book recommendations, go to *MarketingThumbrules.com* & type in these keyword tags: Collaterals, style, presentation, networking

Professional **Prospecting** Thumb–rule #22

# Place your name badge on the right lapel.

*How important is this thumb-rule to you?* ☆ ☆ ☆ ☆ ☆

*How many different ways can you use this thumb-rule? Share it here:*

ACTION ITEMS:

*How well do you practice this thumb-rule?* low 1 2 3 4 5 6 high

For explanations, anecdotes, and book recommendations, go to *MarketingThumbrules.com* & type in these keyword tags: Character, networking, style, presentation

Professional **Prospecting** Thumb-rule #23

## Computerize your contact database.

*How important is this thumb-rule to you?* ☆ ☆ ☆ ☆ ☆

*What kind of habits does this thumb-rule inspire for you? Write it below:*

ACTION ITEMS:

*How well do you practice this thumb-rule?* low 1  2  3  4  5  6  high

For explanations, anecdotes, and book recommendations,
go to *MarketingThumbrules.com* & type in these keyword tags:
Community, technology, relationships, networking

Professional **Prospecting** Thumb–rule #24

## White space and silence helps them absorb your content.

*How important is this thumb-rule to you?* ☆ ☆ ☆ ☆ ☆

*How many different ways can you use this thumb-rule? Share it here:*

ACTION ITEMS:

*How well do you practice this thumb-rule?* low 1 2 3 4 5 6 high

For explanations, anecdotes, and book recommendations, go to *MarketingThumbrules.com* & type in these keyword tags: Collaterals, presentation, message

Professional **Prospecting** Thumb-rule #25

## Exploit the special dates & seasons of your niche target market.

*How important is this thumb-rule to you?* ☆ ☆ ☆ ☆ ☆

*What kind of habits does this thumb-rule inspire for you? Write it below:*

---

---

---

---

ACTION ITEMS:

---

---

*How well do you practice this thumb-rule?* low 1 2 3 4 5 6 high

For explanations, anecdotes, and book recommendations, go to *MarketingThumbrules.com* & type in these keyword tags: Currency, Community, catchphrase, message

Professional **Prospecting** Thumb-rule #26

> ## Despite initial response, advertising often needs at least 7 impressions to persuade momentum.

*How important is this thumb-rule to you?* ☆ ☆ ☆ ☆ ☆

*How many different ways can you use this thumb-rule? Share it here:*

ACTION ITEMS:

*How well do you practice this thumb-rule?* low 1 2 3 4 5 6 high

For explanations, anecdotes, and book recommendations, go to *MarketingThumbrules.com* & type in these keyword tags: Channels, Consistency, message, recognition, results

Professional **Prospecting** Thumb-rule #27

**Put your contact information
on everything, all the time.**

*How important is this thumb-rule to you?* ☆ ☆ ☆ ☆ ☆

*What kind of habits does this thumb-rule inspire for you? Write it below:*

ACTION ITEMS:

*How well do you practice this thumb-rule?* low 1 2 3 4 5 6 high

For explanations, anecdotes, and book recommendations,
go to *MarketingThumbrules.com* & type in these keyword tags:
Consistency, Collaterals, recognition, results

Professional **Prospecting** Thumb–rule #28

> # Tradeshows can be a direct money-making point of sale.

*How important is this thumb-rule to you?* ☆ ☆ ☆ ☆ ☆

*How many different ways can you use this thumb-rule? Share it here:*

ACTION ITEMS:

*How well do you practice this thumb-rule?* low 1 2 3 4 5 6 high

For explanations, anecdotes, and book recommendations, go to *MarketingThumbrules.com* & type in these keyword tags: Channels, money

Professional **Prospecting** Thumb–rule #29

# Offer a clear, simple, and time-bound call to action.

*How important is this thumb-rule to you?* ☆ ☆ ☆ ☆ ☆

*What kind of habits does this thumb-rule inspire for you? Write it below:*

ACTION ITEMS:

*How well do you practice this thumb-rule?* low 1 2 3 4 5 6 high

For explanations, anecdotes, and book recommendations, go to *MarketingThumbrules.com* & type in these keyword tags: Controls, message, results

Professional **Prospecting** Thumb–rule #30

---

## Many newspapers, magazines, newsletters, & website calendars will promote your events for free.

---

*How important is this thumb-rule to you?* ☆ ☆ ☆ ☆ ☆

*How many different ways can you use this thumb-rule? Share it here:*

ACTION ITEMS:

*How well do you practice this thumb-rule?* low 1 2 3 4 5 6 high

For explanations, anecdotes, and book recommendations, go to *MarketingThumbrules.com* & type in these keyword tags: Channels, publishing

Professional **Prospecting** Thumb-rule #31

# Update your sales funnel every week.

*How important is this thumb-rule to you?* ☆ ☆ ☆ ☆ ☆

*What kind of habits does this thumb-rule inspire for you? Write it below:*

ACTION ITEMS:

*How well do you practice this thumb-rule?* low  1  2  3  4  5  6  high

For explanations, anecdotes, and book recommendations, go to *MarketingThumbrules.com* & type in these keyword tags: Controls, goals, results

Professional **Prospecting** Thumb-rule #32

# How much does it cost to acquire a new prospect? ...A new client?

*How important is this thumb-rule to you?* ☆ ☆ ☆ ☆ ☆

*How many different ways can you use this thumb-rule? Share it here:*

ACTION ITEMS:

*How well do you practice this thumb-rule?* low 1 2 3 4 5 6 high

For explanations, anecdotes, and book recommendations, go to *MarketingThumbrules.com* & type in these keyword tags: Controls, money, results

Professional **Prospecting** Thumb–rule #33

## How long is your sales cycle?
## What is your closing ratio?

*How important is this thumb-rule to you?*  ☆ ☆ ☆ ☆ ☆

*What kind of habits does this thumb-rule inspire for you? Write it below:*

ACTION ITEMS:

*How well do you practice this thumb-rule?* low  1  2  3  4  5  6  high

For explanations, anecdotes, and book recommendations, go to *MarketingThumbrules.com* & type in these keyword tags: Controls, planning, results

Professional **Prospecting** Thumb-rule #34

## E-blasts should avoid words like "free," "sex," etc. to evade basic spam blockers. (Start subjects with "re:" or "fwd:" for slightly better odds.)

How important is this thumb-rule to you? ☆ ☆ ☆ ☆ ☆

How many different ways can you use this thumb-rule? Share it here:

ACTION ITEMS:

How well do you practice this thumb-rule? low 1 2 3 4 5 6 high

For explanations, anecdotes, and book recommendations, go to *MarketingThumbrules.com* & type in these keyword tags: Controls, technology, message

Professional **Prospecting** Thumb–rule #35

## Don't assume your prospects will think through your advertisements.

*How important is this thumb-rule to you?* ☆ ☆ ☆ ☆ ☆

*What kind of habits does this thumb-rule inspire for you? Write it below:*

---

---

---

---

ACTION ITEMS:

---

---

*How well do you practice this thumb-rule?* low 1  2  3  4  5  6  high

For explanations, anecdotes, and book recommendations, go to *MarketingThumbrules.com* & type in these keyword tags: Collaterals, Controls, message

Professional **Prospecting** Thumb-rule #36

## Make friends with gatekeepers.

*How important is this thumb-rule to you?* ☆ ☆ ☆ ☆ ☆

*How many different ways can you use this thumb-rule? Share it here:*

ACTION ITEMS:

*How well do you practice this thumb-rule?* low 1 2 3 4 5 6 high

For explanations, anecdotes, and book recommendations, go to *MarketingThumbrules.com* & type in these keyword tags: Channels, relationships, people, smile

Professional **Prospecting** Thumb–rule #37

## Make your website interactive. (Make everything interactive.)

*How important is this thumb-rule to you?* ☆ ☆ ☆ ☆ ☆

*What kind of habits does this thumb-rule inspire for you? Write it below:*

ACTION ITEMS:

*How well do you practice this thumb-rule?* low 1 2 3 4 5 6 high

For explanations, anecdotes, and book recommendations, go to *MarketingThumbrules.com* & type in these keyword tags: Collaterals, Community, experience, technology

Professional **Prospecting** Thumb-rule #38

> # Right-click on your competitor's website to see their meta tags. Use Alexa.com to discover their in-links.

*How important is this thumb-rule to you?* ☆ ☆ ☆ ☆ ☆

*How many different ways can you use this thumb-rule? Share it here:*

ACTION ITEMS:

*How well do you practice this thumb-rule?* low 1 2 3 4 5 6 high

For explanations, anecdotes, and book recommendations, go to *MarketingThumbrules.com* & type in these keyword tags: Controls, technology, competition

Professional **Prospecting** Thumb–rule #39

> # Keep a running record of prospects' and clients' F.A.Q's. It's the best marketing content and room for improvement.

*How important is this thumb-rule to you?* ☆ ☆ ☆ ☆ ☆

*What kind of habits does this thumb-rule inspire for you? Write it below:*

---

---

---

---

ACTION ITEMS:

---

---

*How well do you practice this thumb-rule?* low 1 2 3 4 5 6 high

For explanations, anecdotes, and book recommendations, go to *MarketingThumbrules.com* & type in these keyword tags: Controls, Collaterals, message

Professional **Prospecting** Thumb-rule #40

> # Buy a color laser printer. Use glossy paper (made for color lasers).

*How important is this thumb-rule to you?* ☆ ☆ ☆ ☆ ☆

*How many different ways can you use this thumb-rule? Share it here:*

ACTION ITEMS:

*How well do you practice this thumb-rule?* low 1 2 3 4 5 6 high

For explanations, anecdotes, and book recommendations, go to *MarketingThumbrules.com* & type in these keyword tags: Collaterals, technology

Professional **Prospecting** Thumb-rule #41

## Print 4 quick postcards on a standard 8½ x 11 piece of cardstock.

*How important is this thumb-rule to you?* ☆ ☆ ☆ ☆ ☆

*What kind of habits does this thumb-rule inspire for you? Write it below:*

---

---

---

---

ACTION ITEMS:

---

---

*How well do you practice this thumb-rule?* low 1  2  3  4  5  6  high

For explanations, anecdotes, and book recommendations, go to *MarketingThumbrules.com* & type in these keyword tags: Collaterals, technology

Professional **Prospecting** Thumb–rule #42

# Don't print your own business cards.

*How important is this thumb-rule to you?* ☆ ☆ ☆ ☆ ☆

*How many different ways can you use this thumb-rule? Share it here:*

ACTION ITEMS:

*How well do you practice this thumb-rule?* low 1 2 3 4 5 6 high

For explanations, anecdotes, and book recommendations, go to *MarketingThumbrules.com* & type in these keyword tags: Controls, Collaterals, technology

Professional **Prospecting** Thumb-rule #43

> # Your contacts will use your business cards above all other collaterals. Make it stand out; offer value.

*How important is this thumb-rule to you?* ☆ ☆ ☆ ☆ ☆

*What kind of habits does this thumb-rule inspire for you? Write it below:*

_____

_____

_____

_____

ACTION ITEMS:

_____

_____

*How well do you practice this thumb-rule?* low 1  2  3  4  5  6  high

For explanations, anecdotes, and book recommendations, go to *MarketingThumbrules.com* & type in these keyword tags: Collaterals, message, compliance

Professional **Prospecting** Thumb-rule #44

> # Put directions to your office on your website (or link to a mapping service, with your address pre-populated.)

*How important is this thumb-rule to you?* ☆ ☆ ☆ ☆ ☆

*How many different ways can you use this thumb-rule? Share it here:*

ACTION ITEMS:

*How well do you practice this thumb-rule?* low  1  2  3  4  5  6  high

For explanations, anecdotes, and book recommendations, go to *MarketingThumbrules.com* & type in these keyword tags: Collaterals, technology

Professional **Prospecting** Thumb–rule #45

## Fold your brochure differently than most... like simple origami.

*How important is this thumb-rule to you?* ☆ ☆ ☆ ☆ ☆

*What kind of habits does this thumb-rule inspire for you? Write it below:*

ACTION ITEMS:

*How well do you practice this thumb-rule?* low 1 2 3 4 5 6 high

For explanations, anecdotes, and book recommendations, go to *MarketingThumbrules.com* & type in these keyword tags: Collaterals, style, experience

Professional **Prospecting** Thumb-rule #46

## Follow-up mailings with phone calls.

*How important is this thumb-rule to you?* ☆ ☆ ☆ ☆ ☆

*How many different ways can you use this thumb-rule? Share it here:*

ACTION ITEMS:

*How well do you practice this thumb-rule?* low 1 2 3 4 5 6 high

For explanations, anecdotes, and book recommendations, go to *MarketingThumbrules.com* & type in these keyword tags: Channels, Controls, results

Professional **Prospecting** Thumb–rule #47

---

# The more tight-knit the niche, and smaller the need, the stronger & faster the W-O-M.

---

*How important is this thumb-rule to you?*  ☆ ☆ ☆ ☆ ☆

*What kind of habits does this thumb-rule inspire for you?  Write it below:*

-----------------------------------------------------------------------

-----------------------------------------------------------------------

-----------------------------------------------------------------------

-----------------------------------------------------------------------

ACTION ITEMS:

-----------------------------------------------------------------------

-----------------------------------------------------------------------

*How well do you practice this thumb-rule?* low  1   2   3   4   5   6  high

For explanations, anecdotes, and book recommendations, go to *MarketingThumbrules.com* & type in these keyword tags: Community, Channels, catchphrase, message, results

Professional **Prospecting** Thumb-rule #48

## If meeting outside their offices, jot down their cell phone numbers.

How important is this thumb-rule to you? ☆ ☆ ☆ ☆ ☆

How many different ways can you use this thumb-rule? Share it here:

ACTION ITEMS:

How well do you practice this thumb-rule? low 1 2 3 4 5 6 high

For explanations, anecdotes, and book recommendations, go to *MarketingThumbrules.com* & type in these keyword tags: Controls, technology, relationships, people

Professional **Prospecting** Thumb–rule #49

---

# Update your collaterals (materials) with your target market community's current colloquialisms, idioms, jargon, and buzzwords.

---

*How important is this thumb-rule to you?* ☆ ☆ ☆ ☆ ☆

*What kind of habits does this thumb-rule inspire for you? Write it below:*

---

ACTION ITEMS:

---

*How well do you practice this thumb-rule?* low 1  2  3  4  5  6  high

For explanations, anecdotes, and book recommendations, go to *MarketingThumbrules.com* & type in these keyword tags: Collaterals, Community, Currency, message

Professional **Prospecting** Thumb-rule #50

> # Be at the right place at the right time: Brand trigger events & tschotchkes to remind them of you.

*How important is this thumb-rule to you?* ☆ ☆ ☆ ☆ ☆

*How many different ways can you use this thumb-rule? Share it here:*

ACTION ITEMS:

*How well do you practice this thumb-rule?* low 1 2 3 4 5 6 high

For explanations, anecdotes, and book recommendations, go to *MarketingThumbrules.com* & type in these keyword tags: Currency, Collaterals, catchphrase, message, relationships

Professional **Prospecting** Thumb-rule #51

## Schedule your annual, monthly, and weekly calendar of regular activities.

*How important is this thumb-rule to you?* ☆ ☆ ☆ ☆ ☆

*What kind of habits does this thumb-rule inspire for you? Write it below:*

ACTION ITEMS:

*How well do you practice this thumb-rule?* low 1 2 3 4 5 6 high

For explanations, anecdotes, and book recommendations, go to *MarketingThumbrules.com* & type in these keyword tags: Controls, Consistency, planning, time

Professional **Prospecting** Thumb–rule #52

> # Pick an open market with clear-cut associations, events, and media. Or start those channels.

*How important is this thumb-rule to you?* ☆ ☆ ☆ ☆ ☆

*How many different ways can you use this thumb-rule? Share it here:*

----

----

----

----

ACTION ITEMS:

----

----

*How well do you practice this thumb-rule?* low  1  2  3  4  5  6  high

For explanations, anecdotes, and book recommendations,
go to *MarketingThumbrules.com* & type in these keyword tags:
Channels, Community, competition, innovation

Professional **Prospecting** Thumb-rule #53

## Have multiple websites, each with its own focus.

*How important is this thumb-rule to you?* ☆ ☆ ☆ ☆ ☆

*What kind of habits does this thumb-rule inspire for you? Write it below:*

ACTION ITEMS:

*How well do you practice this thumb-rule?* low 1 2 3 4 5 6 high

For explanations, anecdotes, and book recommendations, go to *MarketingThumbrules.com* & type in these keyword tags: Collaterals, Controls, technology

Professional **Prospecting** Thumb-rule #54

---

# Give away free stuff as an incentive to collect contact information (especially e-mail addresses).

---

*How important is this thumb-rule to you?* ☆ ☆ ☆ ☆ ☆

*How many different ways can you use this thumb-rule? Share it here:*

.................................................................................................................

.................................................................................................................

.................................................................................................................

.................................................................................................................

ACTION ITEMS:

.................................................................................................................

.................................................................................................................

*How well do you practice this thumb-rule?* low 1 2 3 4 5 6 high

For explanations, anecdotes, and book recommendations,
go to *MarketingThumbrules.com* & type in these keyword tags:
Collaterals, Channels, Controls

Professional **Prospecting** Thumb–rule #55

## Use presentation slides as notes for your speech. Remember: Power Points, not paragraphs.

*How important is this thumb-rule to you?* ☆ ☆ ☆ ☆ ☆

*What kind of habits does this thumb-rule inspire for you? Write it below:*

---

---

---

---

ACTION ITEMS:

---

---

*How well do you practice this thumb-rule?* low 1 2 3 4 5 6 high

For explanations, anecdotes, and book recommendations, go to *MarketingThumbrules.com* & type in these keyword tags: Collaterals, technology, presentation

Professional **Prospecting** Thumb-rule #56

## Allocate a marketing budget.
## Then subdivide it into projects.

*How important is this thumb-rule to you?* ☆ ☆ ☆ ☆ ☆

*How many different ways can you use this thumb-rule? Share it here:*

ACTION ITEMS:

*How well do you practice this thumb-rule?* low 1  2  3  4  5  6 high

For explanations, anecdotes, and book recommendations,
go to *MarketingThumbrules.com* & type in these keyword tags:
Controls, money, planning, prioritize

Professional **Prospecting** Thumb-rule #57

## Invite people to attend the tradeshow where you're exhibiting.

*How important is this thumb-rule to you?* ☆ ☆ ☆ ☆ ☆

*What kind of habits does this thumb-rule inspire for you? Write it below:*

--------------------------------------------------

--------------------------------------------------

--------------------------------------------------

--------------------------------------------------

ACTION ITEMS:

--------------------------------------------------

--------------------------------------------------

*How well do you practice this thumb-rule?* low  1   2   3   4   5   6  high

For explanations, anecdotes, and book recommendations, go to *MarketingThumbrules.com* & type in these keyword tags: Channels, Community, recognition, relationships, networking

Professional **Prospecting** Thumb-rule #58

## Study infomercials as templates.

*How important is this thumb-rule to you?* ☆ ☆ ☆ ☆ ☆

*How many different ways can you use this thumb-rule? Share it here:*

ACTION ITEMS:

*How well do you practice this thumb-rule?* low 1 2 3 4 5 6 high

For explanations, anecdotes, and book recommendations, go to *MarketingThumbrules.com* & type in these keyword tags: Collaterals, message

Professional **Prospecting** Thumb-rule #59

# Co-brand or co-market only with those equal or stronger in pull.

*How important is this thumb-rule to you?* ☆ ☆ ☆ ☆ ☆

*What kind of habits does this thumb-rule inspire for you? Write it below:*

ACTION ITEMS:

*How well do you practice this thumb-rule?* low 1 2 3 4 5 6 high

For explanations, anecdotes, and book recommendations, go to *MarketingThumbrules.com* & type in these keyword tags: Channels, relationships

Professional **Prospecting** Thumb–rule #60

> ## 'Perfection' stands still while 'Good Enough' makes money.

*How important is this thumb-rule to you?* ☆ ☆ ☆ ☆ ☆

*How many different ways can you use this thumb-rule? Share it here:*

ACTION ITEMS:

*How well do you practice this thumb-rule?* low 1 2 3 4 5 6 high

For explanations, anecdotes, and book recommendations,
go to *MarketingThumbrules.com* & type in these keyword tags:
Collaterals, mindset, presentation, results

Professional **Prospecting** Thumb-rule #61

# Charge for your seminars to keep out the riff-raff.

*How important is this thumb-rule to you?* ☆ ☆ ☆ ☆ ☆

*What kind of habits does this thumb-rule inspire for you? Write it below:*

ACTION ITEMS:

*How well do you practice this thumb-rule?* low 1 2 3 4 5 6 high

For explanations, anecdotes, and book recommendations, go to *MarketingThumbrules.com* & type in these keyword tags: Controls, money, people, presentation

Professional **Prospecting** Thumb-rule #62

# Doing something is better than doing nothing.

*How important is this thumb-rule to you?* ☆ ☆ ☆ ☆ ☆

*How many different ways can you use this thumb-rule? Share it here:*

ACTION ITEMS:

*How well do you practice this thumb-rule?* low 1 2 3 4 5 6 high

For explanations, anecdotes, and book recommendations, go to *MarketingThumbrules.com* & type in these keyword tags: Channels, style, results

Professional **Prospecting** Thumb–rule #63

> # If they ask you to send them something by mail, don't bother. Instead, e-mail them consistently.

*How important is this thumb-rule to you?* ☆ ☆ ☆ ☆ ☆

*What kind of habits does this thumb-rule inspire for you? Write it below:*

---

---

---

---

ACTION ITEMS:

---

---

*How well do you practice this thumb-rule?* low 1  2  3  4  5  6 high

For explanations, anecdotes, and book recommendations,
go to *MarketingThumbrules.com* & type in these keyword tags:
Channels, Consistency, technology, relationships

Professional **Prospecting** Thumb-rule #64

> # Burn your own 'audio-book' CD and customize its cover label. It can be a product for sale or a giveaway.

How important is this thumb-rule to you?  ☆ ☆ ☆ ☆ ☆

How many different ways can you use this thumb-rule? Share it here:

ACTION ITEMS:

How well do you practice this thumb-rule?  low  1  2  3  4  5  6  high

For explanations, anecdotes, and book recommendations, go to *MarketingThumbrules.com* & type in these keyword tags: Collaterals, technology, reputation, publishing

Professional **Prospecting** Thumb–rule #65

## 300 dpi TIFs for professional print services. 100 dpi GIFs for websites.

*How important is this thumb-rule to you?* ☆ ☆ ☆ ☆ ☆

*What kind of habits does this thumb-rule inspire for you? Write it below:*

---

---

---

---

ACTION ITEMS:

---

---

*How well do you practice this thumb-rule?* low 1 2 3 4 5 6 high

For explanations, anecdotes, and book recommendations, go to *MarketingThumbrules.com* & type in these keyword tags: Collaterals, Controls, technology

Professional **Prospecting** Thumb-rule #66

## Be specific with what you want.

*How important is this thumb-rule to you?* ☆ ☆ ☆ ☆ ☆

*How many different ways can you use this thumb-rule? Share it here:*

ACTION ITEMS:

*How well do you practice this thumb-rule?* low 1 2 3 4 5 6 high

For explanations, anecdotes, and book recommendations,
go to *MarketingThumbrules.com* & type in these keyword tags:
Controls, networking, people, delegation

Professional **Prospecting** Thumb-rule #67

# The folks sitting alone at networking events are often business owners.

*How important is this thumb-rule to you?* ☆ ☆ ☆ ☆ ☆

*What kind of habits does this thumb-rule inspire for you? Write it below:*

_____

_____

_____

_____

ACTION ITEMS:

_____

_____

*How well do you practice this thumb-rule?* low 1 2 3 4 5 6 high

For explanations, anecdotes, and book recommendations, go to *MarketingThumbrules.com* & type in these keyword tags: Community, networking, relationships

Professional **Prospecting** Thumb-rule #68

> # With weekends, holidays, and vacations, there are less than 200 productive days in a year.

*How important is this thumb-rule to you?* ☆ ☆ ☆ ☆ ☆

*How many different ways can you use this thumb-rule? Share it here:*

ACTION ITEMS:

*How well do you practice this thumb-rule?* low 1 2 3 4 5 6 high

For explanations, anecdotes, and book recommendations, go to *MarketingThumbrules.com* & type in these keyword tags: Controls, time, planning, results

Professional **Prospecting** Thumb–rule #69

## Every day is 20% of the work week.

*How important is this thumb-rule to you?* ☆ ☆ ☆ ☆ ☆

*What kind of habits does this thumb-rule inspire for you? Write it below:*

---

---

---

---

ACTION ITEMS:

---

---

*How well do you practice this thumb-rule?* low 1 2 3 4 5 6 high

For explanations, anecdotes, and book recommendations, go to *MarketingThumbrules.com* & type in these keyword tags: Controls, time, prioritize

Professional **Prospecting** Thumb-rule #70

## People have shorter attention spans.

How important is this thumb-rule to you? ☆ ☆ ☆ ☆ ☆

How many different ways can you use this thumb-rule? Share it here:

ACTION ITEMS:

How well do you practice this thumb-rule? low 1 2 3 4 5 6 high

For explanations, anecdotes, and book recommendations,
go to *MarketingThumbrules.com* & type in these keyword tags:
Controls, Catchphrase, people, presentation, message

Professional **Prospecting** Thumb–rule #71

---

# Sidle up to a colleague who's talking to strangers to meet new people.

---

*How important is this thumb-rule to you?* ☆ ☆ ☆ ☆ ☆

*What kind of habits does this thumb-rule inspire for you? Write it below:*

---

ACTION ITEMS:

---

*How well do you practice this thumb-rule?* low 1 2 3 4 5 6 high

For explanations, anecdotes, and book recommendations, go to *MarketingThumbrules.com* & type in these keyword tags: Channels, networking, relationships

Professional **Prospecting** Thumb-rule #72

> # Don't sit with people you know at networking events.

How important is this thumb-rule to you? ☆ ☆ ☆ ☆ ☆

How many different ways can you use this thumb-rule? Share it here:

......................................................................

......................................................................

......................................................................

......................................................................

ACTION ITEMS:

......................................................................

......................................................................

How well do you practice this thumb-rule? low 1 2 3 4 5 6 high

For explanations, anecdotes, and book recommendations, go to *MarketingThumbrules.com* & type in these keyword tags: Controls, networking, relationships, results

Professional **Prospecting** Thumb–rule #73

## "Hi. My name is .......
## So you belong to this group?
## What kind of work do you do?"

*How important is this thumb-rule to you?* ☆ ☆ ☆ ☆ ☆

*What kind of habits does this thumb-rule inspire for you? Write it below:*

ACTION ITEMS:

*How well do you practice this thumb-rule?* low 1 2 3 4 5 6 high

For explanations, anecdotes, and book recommendations, go to *MarketingThumbrules.com* & type in these keyword tags: Charisma, leadership, networking, relationships

Professional **Prospecting** Thumb-rule #74

> ## Ask colleagues to send out e-mails about your events.

How important is this thumb-rule to you? ☆ ☆ ☆ ☆ ☆

How many different ways can you use this thumb-rule? Share it here:

---

---

---

---

ACTION ITEMS:

---

---

How well do you practice this thumb-rule? low 1  2  3  4  5  6  high

For explanations, anecdotes, and book recommendations, go to *MarketingThumbrules.com* & type in these keyword tags: Channels, relationships, technology

Professional **Prospecting** Thumb-rule #75

## Tradeshow exhibitors resent 'walkers' selling to them. On the other hand, fellow co-exhibitors make great prospects.

*How important is this thumb-rule to you?* ☆ ☆ ☆ ☆ ☆

*What kind of habits does this thumb-rule inspire for you? Write it below:*

-------------------------------------------------------------------

-------------------------------------------------------------------

-------------------------------------------------------------------

-------------------------------------------------------------------

ACTION ITEMS:

-------------------------------------------------------------------

-------------------------------------------------------------------

*How well do you practice this thumb-rule?* low 1 2 3 4 5 6 high

For explanations, anecdotes, and book recommendations, go to *MarketingThumbrules.com* & type in these keyword tags: Channels, people, relationships

Professional **Prospecting** Thumb-rule #76

**Make a fun & memorable impression:
USPS allows you to stamp postage
right on any item, without a box
(safe and unbreakable, like a ball).**

*How important is this thumb-rule to you?* ☆ ☆ ☆ ☆ ☆

*How many different ways can you use this thumb-rule? Share it here:*

ACTION ITEMS:

*How well do you practice this thumb-rule?* low 1 2 3 4 5 6 high

For explanations, anecdotes, and book recommendations,
go to *MarketingThumbrules.com* & type in these keyword tags:
Collaterals, Channels, recognition, smile, presentation

Professional **Prospecting** Thumb–rule #77

> # It's a numbers game.
> # Keep your dashboard in front of you.

*How important is this thumb-rule to you?* ☆ ☆ ☆ ☆ ☆

*What kind of habits does this thumb-rule inspire for you? Write it below:*

---

---

---

---

ACTION ITEMS:

---

---

*How well do you practice this thumb-rule?* low 1 2 3 4 5 6 high

For explanations, anecdotes, and book recommendations, go to *MarketingThumbrules.com* & type in these keyword tags:
Controls, goals, results, prioritize, money, mindset

Professional **Prospecting** Thumb-rule #78

## Buy mispelled domain names and keywords.

How important is this thumb-rule to you? ☆ ☆ ☆ ☆ ☆

How many different ways can you use this thumb-rule? Share it here:

ACTION ITEMS:

How well do you practice this thumb-rule? low  1  2  3  4  5  6  high

For explanations, anecdotes, and book recommendations, go to *MarketingThumbrules.com* & type in these keyword tags: Channels, Collaterals, Currency, technology

Professional **Prospecting** Thumb-rule #79

## Use numbers in your seminar and book titles.

*How important is this thumb-rule to you?* ☆ ☆ ☆ ☆ ☆

*What kind of habits does this thumb-rule inspire for you? Write it below:*

----

----

----

----

ACTION ITEMS:

----

----

*How well do you practice this thumb-rule?* low 1 2 3 4 5 6 high

For explanations, anecdotes, and book recommendations, go to *MarketingThumbrules.com* & type in these keyword tags: Collaterals, Currency, Catchphrase, message, publishing

274 *Marketing Thumb-rules*

Professional **Prospecting** Thumb–rule #80

> # Write out the 1-to-3-word phrases that your prospects search for. Sprinkle excessively.

How important is this thumb-rule to you? ☆ ☆ ☆ ☆ ☆

How many different ways can you use this thumb-rule? Share it here:

ACTION ITEMS:

How well do you practice this thumb-rule? low 1 2 3 4 5 6 high

For explanations, anecdotes, and book recommendations,
go to *MarketingThumbrules.com* & type in these keyword tags:
Collaterals, Catchphrase, message, technology

Professional **Prospecting** Thumb-rule #81

# Talk to strangers.

*How important is this thumb-rule to you?* ☆ ☆ ☆ ☆ ☆

*What kind of habits does this thumb-rule inspire for you? Write it below:*

---

ACTION ITEMS:

---

*How well do you practice this thumb-rule?* low 1 2 3 4 5 6 high

For explanations, anecdotes, and book recommendations,
go to *MarketingThumbrules.com* & type in these keyword tags:
Channels, Controls, networking

Professional **Prospecting** Thumb–rule #82

## Posture your sales process: "This is the way I work…"

*How important is this thumb-rule to you?* ☆ ☆ ☆ ☆ ☆

*How many different ways can you use this thumb-rule? Share it here:*

ACTION ITEMS:

*How well do you practice this thumb-rule?* low 1 2 3 4 5 6 high

For explanations, anecdotes, and book recommendations, go to *MarketingThumbrules.com* & type in these keyword tags: Channels, relationships, networking

Professional **Prospecting** Thumb-rule #83

> # There doesn't need to be any (e.g., summer) lulls in your practice.

How important is this thumb-rule to you?  ☆ ☆ ☆ ☆ ☆

What kind of habits does this thumb-rule inspire for you? Write it below:

---

---

---

---

ACTION ITEMS:

---

---

How well do you practice this thumb-rule? low 1 2 3 4 5 6 high

For explanations, anecdotes, and book recommendations, go to *MarketingThumbrules.com* & type in these keyword tags: Consistency, Currency, goals, vision, mindset

Professional **Prospecting** Thumb-rule #84

> # Put everybody you've ever known on your e-mail list: Past co-workers, prospects, vendors, & neighbors.

*How important is this thumb-rule to you?* ☆ ☆ ☆ ☆ ☆

*How many different ways can you use this thumb-rule? Share it here:*

ACTION ITEMS:

*How well do you practice this thumb-rule?* low 1 2 3 4 5 6 high

For explanations, anecdotes, and book recommendations, go to *MarketingThumbrules.com* & type in these keyword tags: Community, Channels, relationships, networking, technology

Professional **Prospecting** Thumb-rule #85

## You don't know, if you don't try: Test market. Measure, improve, duplicate.

*How important is this thumb-rule to you?* ☆ ☆ ☆ ☆ ☆

*What kind of habits does this thumb-rule inspire for you? Write it below:*

ACTION ITEMS:

*How well do you practice this thumb-rule?* low 1 2 3 4 5 6 high

For explanations, anecdotes, and book recommendations, go to *MarketingThumbrules.com* & type in these keyword tags: Controls, results, system

Professional **Prospecting** Thumb-rule #86

# Different sized, colored, & see-through envelopes attract attention.

*How important is this thumb-rule to you?* ☆ ☆ ☆ ☆ ☆

*How many different ways can you use this thumb-rule? Share it here:*

ACTION ITEMS:

*How well do you practice this thumb-rule?* low 1 2 3 4 5 6 high

For explanations, anecdotes, and book recommendations, go to *MarketingThumbrules.com* & type in these keyword tags: Collaterals, recognition, style

Professional **Prospecting** Thumb-rule #87

> # Unqualified prospects only have 4 objections: They don't believe you. They can't afford you. They don't have urgency. They don't need you.

*How important is this thumb-rule to you?* ☆ ☆ ☆ ☆ ☆

*What kind of habits does this thumb-rule inspire for you? Write it below:*

---

---

---

---

ACTION ITEMS:

---

---

*How well do you practice this thumb-rule?* low 1 2 3 4 5 6 high

For explanations, anecdotes, and book recommendations, go to *MarketingThumbrules.com* & type in these keyword tags: Controls, Channels, message

Professional **Prospecting** Thumb–rule #88

---

# Interrupt. Stop 'em in their tracks.
# Shock. Grab time & attention.

---

*How important is this thumb-rule to you?* ☆ ☆ ☆ ☆ ☆

*How many different ways can you use this thumb-rule? Share it here:*

ACTION ITEMS:

*How well do you practice this thumb-rule?* low 1 2 3 4 5 6 high

For explanations, anecdotes, and book recommendations,
go to *MarketingThumbrules.com* & type in these keyword tags:
Currency, Catchphrase, style, presentation, experience

Professional **Prospecting** Thumb–rule #89

> # Give referrals to them first, without the expectation of getting.

*How important is this thumb-rule to you?* ☆ ☆ ☆ ☆ ☆

*What kind of habits does this thumb-rule inspire for you? Write it below:*

ACTION ITEMS:

*How well do you practice this thumb-rule?* low 1 2 3 4 5 6 high

For explanations, anecdotes, and book recommendations, go to *MarketingThumbrules.com* & type in these keyword tags: Channels, networking, relationships

Professional **Prospecting** Thumb-rule #90

---

# 83% are visual learners; 11% learn by hearing.

---

*How important is this thumb-rule to you?* ☆ ☆ ☆ ☆ ☆

*How many different ways can you use this thumb-rule? Share it here:*

. . . . . . . . . . . . . . . . . . . . . . . . . . . . . . . . . . . . . . . . . . . . . . . . . . . . . . . . . . . . . . . . . . . . . . . . .

. . . . . . . . . . . . . . . . . . . . . . . . . . . . . . . . . . . . . . . . . . . . . . . . . . . . . . . . . . . . . . . . . . . . . . . . .

. . . . . . . . . . . . . . . . . . . . . . . . . . . . . . . . . . . . . . . . . . . . . . . . . . . . . . . . . . . . . . . . . . . . . . . . .

. . . . . . . . . . . . . . . . . . . . . . . . . . . . . . . . . . . . . . . . . . . . . . . . . . . . . . . . . . . . . . . . . . . . . . . . .

. . . . . . . . . . . . . . . . . . . . . . . . . . . . . . . . . . . . . . . . . . . . . . . . . . . . . . . . . . . . . . . . . . . . . . . . .

ACTION ITEMS:

. . . . . . . . . . . . . . . . . . . . . . . . . . . . . . . . . . . . . . . . . . . . . . . . . . . . . . . . . . . . . . . . . . . . . . . . .

. . . . . . . . . . . . . . . . . . . . . . . . . . . . . . . . . . . . . . . . . . . . . . . . . . . . . . . . . . . . . . . . . . . . . . . . .

*How well do you practice this thumb-rule?* low 1 2 3 4 5 6 high

For explanations, anecdotes, and book recommendations,
go to *MarketingThumbrules.com* & type in these keyword tags:
Collaterals, Community, people, experience

Professional **Prospecting** Thumb-rule #91

---

# We remember only 10% of what we read; 20% of what we hear; 30% of what we see. We remember 90% of what we say as we do something.

---

*How important is this thumb-rule to you?* ☆ ☆ ☆ ☆ ☆

*What kind of habits does this thumb-rule inspire for you? Write it below:*

ACTION ITEMS:

*How well do you practice this thumb-rule?* low 1  2  3  4  5  6  high

For explanations, anecdotes, and book recommendations, go to *MarketingThumbrules.com* & type in these keyword tags: Collaterals, Community, people, experience

Professional **Prospecting** Thumb-rule #92

# Describe your target market with the categories, labels, or titles they call themselves.

*How important is this thumb-rule to you?* ☆ ☆ ☆ ☆ ☆

*How many different ways can you use this thumb-rule? Share it here:*

ACTION ITEMS:

*How well do you practice this thumb-rule?* low 1 2 3 4 5 6 high

For explanations, anecdotes, and book recommendations, go to *MarketingThumbrules.com* & type in these keyword tags: Community, people, message

Professional **Prospecting** Thumb–rule #93

> # Write out your 1-on-1 and phone scripts in bullet points.

*How important is this thumb-rule to you?* ☆ ☆ ☆ ☆ ☆

*What kind of habits does this thumb-rule inspire for you?* *Write it below:*

ACTION ITEMS:

*How well do you practice this thumb-rule?* low 1 2 3 4 5 6 high

For explanations, anecdotes, and book recommendations, go to *MarketingThumbrules.com* & type in these keyword tags: Channels, presentation, planning, system, delegation

Professional **Prospecting** Thumb–rule #94

## Don't blast your e-newsletter on Mondays (especially mornings).

*How important is this thumb-rule to you?* ☆ ☆ ☆ ☆ ☆

*How many different ways can you use this thumb-rule? Share it here:*

........................................................................................................

........................................................................................................

........................................................................................................

........................................................................................................

ACTION ITEMS:

........................................................................................................

........................................................................................................

*How well do you practice this thumb-rule?* low 1 2 3 4 5 6 high

For explanations, anecdotes, and book recommendations, go to *MarketingThumbrules.com* & type in these keyword tags: Controls, people, technology, time

Professional **Prospecting** Thumb–rule #95

---

# Don't hold events on Mondays.
# Use Mondays for reminders.

---

*How important is this thumb-rule to you?* ☆ ☆ ☆ ☆ ☆

*What kind of habits does this thumb-rule inspire for you? Write it below:*

---

ACTION ITEMS:

---

*How well do you practice this thumb-rule?* low 1 2 3 4 5 6 high

For explanations, anecdotes, and book recommendations,
go to *MarketingThumbrules.com* & type in these keyword tags:
Controls, Currency, networking, presentation, time

Professional **Prospecting** Thumb-rule #96

> # People barely do what's on their 'to-do' lists, let alone yours: Remind persistently, but don't nag.

*How important is this thumb-rule to you?* ☆ ☆ ☆ ☆ ☆

*How many different ways can you use this thumb-rule? Share it here:*

ACTION ITEMS:

*How well do you practice this thumb-rule?* low 1 2 3 4 5 6 high

For explanations, anecdotes, and book recommendations, go to *MarketingThumbrules.com* & type in these keyword tags: Controls, Community, people, planning, time

Professional **Prospecting** Thumb-rule #97

# Quality contacts, over quantity business card exchanges.

*How important is this thumb-rule to you?* ☆ ☆ ☆ ☆ ☆

*What kind of habits does this thumb-rule inspire for you? Write it below:*

---

---

---

---

ACTION ITEMS:

---

---

*How well do you practice this thumb-rule?* low 1 2 3 4 5 6 high

For explanations, anecdotes, and book recommendations, go to *MarketingThumbrules.com* & type in these keyword tags: Community, mindset, time, networking, relationships

Professional **Prospecting** Thumb-rule #98

> # People enjoy eating, drinking, talking, and be entertained.

How important is this thumb-rule to you? ☆ ☆ ☆ ☆ ☆

How many different ways can you use this thumb-rule? Share it here:

ACTION ITEMS:

How well do you practice this thumb-rule? low 1 2 3 4 5 6 high

For explanations, anecdotes, and book recommendations, go to *MarketingThumbrules.com* & type in these keyword tags: Community, people, experience

Ethical **Selling** Thumb-rule #1

# Give out worksheets.

*How important is this thumb-rule to you?* ☆ ☆ ☆ ☆ ☆

*What's your experience with this thumb-rule? Describe it here:*

---

---

---

---

ACTION ITEMS:

---

---

*How well do you practice this thumb-rule?* low 1 2 3 4 5 6 high

For explanations, anecdotes, and book recommendations, go to *MarketingThumbrules.com* & type in these keyword tags: Collaterals, Competency, experience, presentation

Ethical **Selling** Thumb-rule #2

# ABC = Always Be Closing.

*How important is this thumb-rule to you?* ☆ ☆ ☆ ☆ ☆

*What challenges prevent others from following this thumb-rule? Share it:*

ACTION ITEMS:

*How well do you practice this thumb-rule?* low 1 2 3 4 5 6 high

For explanations, anecdotes, and book recommendations, go to *MarketingThumbrules.com* & type in these keyword tags: Channels, competition, message, mindset, results

Ethical **Selling** Thumb–rule #3

# Other people are always thinking, 'WIIFM'

*How important is this thumb-rule to you?* ☆ ☆ ☆ ☆ ☆

*What's your experience with this thumb-rule? Describe it here:*

ACTION ITEMS:

*How well do you practice this thumb-rule?* low 1 2 3 4 5 6 high

For explanations, anecdotes, and book recommendations, go to *MarketingThumbrules.com* & type in these keyword tags: Community, Collaterals, people, message, presentation, mindset

Ethical **Selling** Thumb-rule #4

# Listening well is necessary for questioning well.

*How important is this thumb-rule to you?* ☆ ☆ ☆ ☆ ☆

*What challenges prevent others from following this thumb-rule? Share it:*

ACTION ITEMS:

*How well do you practice this thumb-rule?* low 1 2 3 4 5 6 high

For explanations, anecdotes, and book recommendations,
go to *MarketingThumbrules.com* & type in these keyword tags:
Character, mindset, questions

Ethical **Selling** Thumb–rule #5

## Frustrations are just symptoms of systemic problems.

*How important is this thumb-rule to you?* ☆ ☆ ☆ ☆ ☆

*What's your experience with this thumb-rule? Describe it here:*

ACTION ITEMS:

*How well do you practice this thumb-rule?* low 1  2  3  4  5  6  high

For explanations, anecdotes, and book recommendations, go to *MarketingThumbrules.com* & type in these keyword tags: Controls, system, people, mindset

Ethical **Selling** Thumb-rule #6

# In negotiations, he who talks the most, loses. (Ask questions. Shut up & listen.)

*How important is this thumb-rule to you?* ☆ ☆ ☆ ☆ ☆

*What challenges prevent others from following this thumb-rule? Share it:*

ACTION ITEMS:

*How well do you practice this thumb-rule?* low 1 2 3 4 5 6 high

For explanations, anecdotes, and book recommendations,
go to *MarketingThumbrules.com* & type in these keyword tags:
Competency, questions, presentation, results

Ethical **Selling** Thumb–rule #7

# Feel, Felt, Found.

*How important is this thumb-rule to you?* ☆ ☆ ☆ ☆ ☆

*What's your experience with this thumb-rule? Describe it here:*

---

---

---

---

ACTION ITEMS:

---

---

*How well do you practice this thumb-rule?* low 1 2 3 4 5 6 high

For explanations, anecdotes, and book recommendations, go to *MarketingThumbrules.com* & type in these keyword tags: Community, Character, presentation

Ethical **Selling** Thumb–rule #8

# Don't get emotionally attached to any one opportunity.

*How important is this thumb-rule to you?* ☆ ☆ ☆ ☆ ☆

*What challenges prevent others from following this thumb-rule? Share it:*

ACTION ITEMS:

*How well do you practice this thumb-rule?* low 1 2 3 4 5 6 high

For explanations, anecdotes, and book recommendations,
go to *MarketingThumbrules.com* & type in these keyword tags:
Character, Controls, mindset

Ethical **Selling** Thumb–rule #9

> # Everybody feels they are right from their own perspective.

*How important is this thumb-rule to you?* ☆ ☆ ☆ ☆ ☆

*What's your experience with this thumb-rule? Describe it here:*

------------------------------------------------------------

------------------------------------------------------------

------------------------------------------------------------

------------------------------------------------------------

ACTION ITEMS:

------------------------------------------------------------

------------------------------------------------------------

*How well do you practice this thumb-rule?* low 1 2 3 4 5 6 high

For explanations, anecdotes, and book recommendations,
go to *MarketingThumbrules.com* & type in these keyword tags:
Community, mindset, people

Ethical **Selling** Thumb-rule #10

## Answer a question with a question.

*How important is this thumb-rule to you?* ☆ ☆ ☆ ☆ ☆

*What challenges prevent others from following this thumb-rule? Share it:*

ACTION ITEMS:

*How well do you practice this thumb-rule?* low  1  2  3  4  5  6  high

For explanations, anecdotes, and book recommendations,
go to *MarketingThumbrules.com* & type in these keyword tags:
Controls, presentation, questions

Ethical **Selling** Thumb-rule #11

## Book a meeting from a meeting.

*How important is this thumb-rule to you?* ☆ ☆ ☆ ☆ ☆

*What's your experience with this thumb-rule? Describe it here:*

-------------------------------------------------------------------

-------------------------------------------------------------------

-------------------------------------------------------------------

-------------------------------------------------------------------

ACTION ITEMS:

-------------------------------------------------------------------

-------------------------------------------------------------------

*How well do you practice this thumb-rule?* low 1  2  3  4  5  6  high

For explanations, anecdotes, and book recommendations,
go to *MarketingThumbrules.com* & type in these keyword tags:
Channels, Consistency, relationships, presentation

Ethical **Selling** Thumb-rule #12

# Market to the end-user.
# Sell to the buyer.

*How important is this thumb-rule to you?* ☆ ☆ ☆ ☆ ☆

*What challenges prevent others from following this thumb-rule? Share it:*

---

ACTION ITEMS:

---

*How well do you practice this thumb-rule?* low 1 2 3 4 5 6 high

For explanations, anecdotes, and book recommendations,
go to *MarketingThumbrules.com* & type in these keyword tags:
Community, Channels, Controls, message, experience

Ethical **Selling** Thumb-rule #13

# Be on time.
# Leave them hungry.

*How important is this thumb-rule to you?* ☆ ☆ ☆ ☆ ☆

*What's your experience with this thumb-rule? Describe it here.*

ACTION ITEMS:

*How well do you practice this thumb-rule?* low 1 2 3 4 5 6 high

For explanations, anecdotes, and book recommendations, go to *MarketingThumbrules.com* & type in these keyword tags: Character, presentation, time, experience

Ethical **Selling** Thumb-rule #14

# A waste of time can still be a learning experience.

*How important is this thumb-rule to you?* ☆ ☆ ☆ ☆ ☆

*What challenges prevent others from following this thumb-rule? Share it:*

ACTION ITEMS:

*How well do you practice this thumb-rule?* low 1 2 3 4 5 6 high

For explanations, anecdotes, and book recommendations,
go to *MarketingThumbrules.com* & type in these keyword tags:
Controls, Character, Competency, time, experience

Ethical **Selling** Thumb–rule #15

# Provide examples, anecdotes, analogies, and metaphors.

*How important is this thumb-rule to you?* ☆ ☆ ☆ ☆ ☆

*What's your experience with this thumb-rule? Describe it here.*

ACTION ITEMS:

*How well do you practice this thumb-rule?* low 1 2 3 4 5 6 high

For explanations, anecdotes, and book recommendations,
go to *MarketingThumbrules.com* & type in these keyword tags:
Collaterals, message, presentation, experience

Ethical **Selling** Thumb–rule #16

# The better your marketing pull, the easier your selling push.

*How important is this thumb-rule to you?* ☆ ☆ ☆ ☆ ☆

*What challenges prevent others from following this thumb-rule? Share it:*

ACTION ITEMS:

*How well do you practice this thumb-rule?* low 1 2 3 4 5 6 high

For explanations, anecdotes, and book recommendations,
go to *MarketingThumbrules.com* & type in these keyword tags:
Controls, Collaterals, Community, Currency, planning, results

Ethical **Selling** Thumb–rule #17

> # Control the conversation:
> ## 'Tell me more about that...'
> ## 'I recommend...'

*How important is this thumb-rule to you?* ☆ ☆ ☆ ☆ ☆

*What's your experience with this thumb-rule? Describe it here:*

---

---

---

---

ACTION ITEMS:

---

---

*How well do you practice this thumb-rule?* low 1  2  3  4  5  6  high

For explanations, anecdotes, and book recommendations,
go to *MarketingThumbrules.com* & type in these keyword tags:
Controls, Character, leadership, experience, presentation

Ethical **Selling** Thumb-rule #18

## Ask open-ended questions.
## Not 'yes/no' questions.

*How important is this thumb-rule to you?* ☆ ☆ ☆ ☆ ☆

*What challenges prevent others from following this thumb-rule? Share it:*

ACTION ITEMS:

*How well do you practice this thumb-rule?* low 1 2 3 4 5 6 high

For explanations, anecdotes, and book recommendations,
go to *MarketingThumbrules.com* & type in these keyword tags:
Charisma, questions, leadership

Ethical **Selling** Thumb–rule #19

> # Back-of-the-room sales.

*How important is this thumb-rule to you?* ☆ ☆ ☆ ☆ ☆

*What's your experience with this thumb-rule? Describe it here:*

---

---

---

---

ACTION ITEMS:

---

---

*How well do you practice this thumb-rule?* low 1  2  3  4  5  6  high

For explanations, anecdotes, and book recommendations,
go to *MarketingThumbrules.com* & type in these keyword tags:
Channels, publishing, events, money

Ethical **Selling** Thumb-rule #20

# When leaving voicemail messages, slowly repeat your phone number twice.

How important is this thumb-rule to you? ☆ ☆ ☆ ☆ ☆

What challenges prevent others from following this thumb-rule? Share it:

ACTION ITEMS:

How well do you practice this thumb-rule? low 1 2 3 4 5 6 high

For explanations, anecdotes, and book recommendations, go to *MarketingThumbrules.com* & type in these keyword tags: Channels, Character, message, technology

Ethical **Selling** Thumb–rule #21

# Research your prospects before you meet with them.

*How important is this thumb-rule to you?* ☆ ☆ ☆ ☆ ☆

*What's your experience with this thumb-rule? Describe it here:*

---

---

---

---

ACTION ITEMS:

---

---

*How well do you practice this thumb-rule?* low 1 2 3 4 5 6 high

For explanations, anecdotes, and book recommendations, go to *MarketingThumbrules.com* & type in these keyword tags: Community, Controls, planning, presentation

Ethical **Selling** Thumb-rule #22

# Customers buy emotionally, then justify rationally.

*How important is this thumb-rule to you?* ☆ ☆ ☆ ☆ ☆

*What challenges prevent others from following this thumb-rule? Share it:*

ACTION ITEMS:

*How well do you practice this thumb-rule?* low 1 2 3 4 5 6 high

For explanations, anecdotes, and book recommendations, go to *MarketingThumbrules.com* & type in these keyword tags: Community, Character, Charisma, people, experience

Ethical **Selling** Thumb–rule #23

# Follow-up within 3 days:
# Strike while the iron's hot.

*How important is this thumb-rule to you?* ☆ ☆ ☆ ☆ ☆

*What's your experience with this thumb-rule? Describe it here:*

ACTION ITEMS:

*How well do you practice this thumb-rule?* low 1 2 3 4 5 6 high

For explanations, anecdotes, and book recommendations,
go to *MarketingThumbrules.com* & type in these keyword tags:
Controls, Currency, prioritize

Ethical **Selling** Thumb-rule #24

# Focus on benefits, not just features.

*How important is this thumb-rule to you?* ☆ ☆ ☆ ☆ ☆

*What challenges prevent others from following this thumb-rule? Share it:*

ACTION ITEMS:

*How well do you practice this thumb-rule?* low 1 2 3 4 5 6 high

For explanations, anecdotes, and book recommendations,
go to *MarketingThumbrules.com* & type in these keyword tags:
Collaterals, message, presentation, people

Ethical **Selling** Thumb-rule #25

# Wine 'em and dine 'em (within ethics and compliance).

*How important is this thumb-rule to you?* ☆ ☆ ☆ ☆ ☆

*What's your experience with this thumb-rule? Describe it here:*

ACTION ITEMS:

*How well do you practice this thumb-rule?* low 1 2 3 4 5 6 high

For explanations, anecdotes, and book recommendations, go to *MarketingThumbrules.com* & type in these keyword tags: Character, Community, relationships, compliance

Ethical **Selling** Thumb–rule #26

# Flip every objection into your value. Bring it up before they do.

*How important is this thumb-rule to you?* ☆ ☆ ☆ ☆ ☆

*What challenges prevent others from following this thumb-rule? Share it:*

ACTION ITEMS:

*How well do you practice this thumb-rule?* low 1 2 3 4 5 6 high

For explanations, anecdotes, and book recommendations,
go to *MarketingThumbrules.com* & type in these keyword tags:
Collaterals, competition, presentation

Ethical **Selling** Thumb-rule #27

## Impress clients, prospects, or colleagues by giving them a copy of your meeting notes.

*How important is this thumb-rule to you?* ☆ ☆ ☆ ☆ ☆

*What's your experience with this thumb-rule? Describe it here:*

ACTION ITEMS:

*How well do you practice this thumb-rule?* low 1 2 3 4 5 6 high

For explanations, anecdotes, and book recommendations, go to *MarketingThumbrules.com* & type in these keyword tags: Competency, Character, Collaterals, presentation

Ethical **Selling** Thumb-rule #28

## Question clients, 'not-for-now' prospects, and non-users for innovative ideas.

*How important is this thumb-rule to you?* ☆ ☆ ☆ ☆ ☆

*What challenges prevent others from following this thumb-rule? Share it:*

-------------------------------------------------------------------

-------------------------------------------------------------------

-------------------------------------------------------------------

-------------------------------------------------------------------

ACTION ITEMS:

-------------------------------------------------------------------

-------------------------------------------------------------------

*How well do you practice this thumb-rule?* low 1 2 3 4 5 6 high

For explanations, anecdotes, and book recommendations, go to *MarketingThumbrules.com* & type in these keyword tags: Currency, questions, innovation

Ethical **Selling** Thumb-rule #29

## Don't hesitate: ASK.

*How important is this thumb-rule to you?* ☆ ☆ ☆ ☆ ☆

*What's your experience with this thumb-rule? Describe it here:*

---

---

---

---

ACTION ITEMS:

---

---

*How well do you practice this thumb-rule?* low 1 2 3 4 5 6 high

For explanations, anecdotes, and book recommendations,
go to *MarketingThumbrules.com* & type in these keyword tags:
Character, mindset, questions

Ethical **Selling** Thumb–rule #30

# Sell (your own) knowledge products at your tradeshow table.

*How important is this thumb-rule to you?* ☆ ☆ ☆ ☆ ☆

*What challenges prevent others from following this thumb-rule? Share it:*

ACTION ITEMS:

*How well do you practice this thumb-rule?* low 1 2 3 4 5 6 high

For explanations, anecdotes, and book recommendations, go to *MarketingThumbrules.com* & type in these keyword tags: Channels, Competency, money, wealth, publishing

Ethical **Selling** Thumb–rule #31

> ## (Old sales rule: Asking your prospects for materials makes them obey you from the beginning.) Use your own branded paper & pen!

*How important is this thumb-rule to you?*  ☆ ☆ ☆ ☆ ☆

*What's your experience with this thumb-rule? Describe it here:*

------------------------------------------------------------------

------------------------------------------------------------------

------------------------------------------------------------------

------------------------------------------------------------------

ACTION ITEMS:

------------------------------------------------------------------

------------------------------------------------------------------

*How well do you practice this thumb-rule?* low  1  2  3  4  5  6  high

For explanations, anecdotes, and book recommendations, go to *MarketingThumbrules.com* & type in these keyword tags: Collaterals, Character, Consistency, experience

Ethical **Selling** Thumb-rule #32

> # Never talk negatively about competitors or colleagues.

How important is this thumb-rule to you? ☆ ☆ ☆ ☆ ☆

What challenges prevent others from following this thumb-rule? Share it:

----

----

----

----

ACTION ITEMS:

----

----

How well do you practice this thumb-rule? low 1 2 3 4 5 6 high

For explanations, anecdotes, and book recommendations, go to *MarketingThumbrules.com* & type in these keyword tags: Character, Controls, competition, reputation, compliance

Ethical **Selling** Thumb-rule #**33**

## Can't beat free.

*How important is this thumb-rule to you?* ☆ ☆ ☆ ☆ ☆

*What's your experience with this thumb-rule? Describe it here:*

ACTION ITEMS:

*How well do you practice this thumb-rule?* low  1  2  3  4  5  6  high

For explanations, anecdotes, and book recommendations,
go to *MarketingThumbrules.com* & type in these keyword tags:
Collaterals, competition, compliance, money

Ethical **Selling** Thumb–rule #34

# Charge more than others.
# Increase your rates.

*How important is this thumb-rule to you?* ☆ ☆ ☆ ☆ ☆

*What challenges prevent others from following this thumb-rule? Share it:*

ACTION ITEMS:

*How well do you practice this thumb-rule?* low 1 2 3 4 5 6 high

For explanations, anecdotes, and book recommendations,
go to *MarketingThumbrules.com* & type in these keyword tags:
Currency, competition, money

Ethical **Selling** Thumb–rule #35

> # Personally involve all the decision makers (and influencers). Don't expect underlings to convey your message or answer well.

*How important is this thumb-rule to you?* ☆ ☆ ☆ ☆ ☆

*What's your experience with this thumb-rule? Describe it here:*

---

---

---

---

ACTION ITEMS:

---

---

*How well do you practice this thumb-rule?* low 1 2 3 4 5 6 high

For explanations, anecdotes, and book recommendations, go to *MarketingThumbrules.com* & type in these keyword tags: Controls, delegation, questions, people, message

Ethical **Selling** Thumb-rule #36

## Look for clues of what you two have in common in how your prospect's office is decorated (or organized).

*How important is this thumb-rule to you?* ☆ ☆ ☆ ☆ ☆

*What challenges prevent others from following this thumb-rule? Share it:*

ACTION ITEMS:

*How well do you practice this thumb-rule?* low 1 2 3 4 5 6 high

For explanations, anecdotes, and book recommendations, go to *MarketingThumbrules.com* & type in these keyword tags: Character, Charisma, Community, relationships, style, values

Ethical **Selling** Thumb–rule #37

## Reverse Psychology, e.g. 'I don't think you're ready for my services,' prompts the prospect to covet what they can't have.

*How important is this thumb-rule to you?*  ☆ ☆ ☆ ☆ ☆

*What's your experience with this thumb-rule? Describe it here:*

---

---

---

---

ACTION ITEMS:

---

---

*How well do you practice this thumb-rule?* low  1  2  3  4  5  6  high

For explanations, anecdotes, and book recommendations,
go to *MarketingThumbrules.com* & type in these keyword tags:
Currency, people, presentation, mindset, results

Ethical **Selling** Thumb-rule #38

# Make 3 attempts to reach a prospect, then move on.

How important is this thumb-rule to you? ☆ ☆ ☆ ☆ ☆

What challenges prevent others from following this thumb-rule? Share it:

ACTION ITEMS:

How well do you practice this thumb-rule? low 1 2 3 4 5 6 high

For explanations, anecdotes, and book recommendations, go to *MarketingThumbrules.com* & type in these keyword tags: Controls, Channels, results

Ethical **Selling** Thumb–rule #39

# Offer deadline-based incentives to close the deal quickly.

*How important is this thumb-rule to you?* ☆ ☆ ☆ ☆ ☆

*What's your experience with this thumb-rule? Describe it here:*

---

---

---

---

ACTION ITEMS:

---

---

*How well do you practice this thumb-rule?* low 1 2 3 4 5 6 high

For explanations, anecdotes, and book recommendations, go to *MarketingThumbrules.com* & type in these keyword tags: Currency, results, money

Ethical **Selling** Thumb-rule #40

## If you have to, break-down fees into the absurd daily cost.

*How important is this thumb-rule to you?* ☆ ☆ ☆ ☆ ☆

*What challenges prevent others from following this thumb-rule? Share it:*

ACTION ITEMS:

*How well do you practice this thumb-rule?* low 1 2 3 4 5 6 high

For explanations, anecdotes, and book recommendations,
go to *MarketingThumbrules.com* & type in these keyword tags:
Controls, money, presentation

Ethical **Selling** Thumb-rule #41

# Ask them to let the referral know that you'll be calling.

*How important is this thumb-rule to you?* ☆ ☆ ☆ ☆ ☆

*What's your experience with this thumb-rule? Describe it here:*

---

ACTION ITEMS:

---

*How well do you practice this thumb-rule?* low 1 2 3 4 5 6 high

For explanations, anecdotes, and book recommendations,
go to *MarketingThumbrules.com* & type in these keyword tags:
Channels, questions, networking

Ethical **Selling** Thumb–rule #42

## Show that you're listening by restating or paraphrasing what was said.

*How important is this thumb-rule to you?* ☆ ☆ ☆ ☆ ☆

*What challenges prevent others from following this thumb-rule? Share it:*

ACTION ITEMS:

*How well do you practice this thumb-rule?* low  1  2  3  4  5  6  high

For explanations, anecdotes, and book recommendations,
go to *MarketingThumbrules.com* & type in these keyword tags:
Character, Charisma, questions, relationships

Ethical **Selling** Thumb-rule #43

# If they can't afford your typical fees, how can you help them get started?

*How important is this thumb-rule to you?* ☆ ☆ ☆ ☆ ☆

*What's your experience with this thumb-rule? Describe it here.*

-----------------------------------------------------------------

-----------------------------------------------------------------

-----------------------------------------------------------------

-----------------------------------------------------------------

ACTION ITEMS:

-----------------------------------------------------------------

-----------------------------------------------------------------

*How well do you practice this thumb-rule?* low  1  2  3  4  5  6  high

For explanations, anecdotes, and book recommendations,
go to *MarketingThumbrules.com* & type in these keyword tags:
Competency, Character, money, relationships, questions

Ethical **Selling** Thumb–rule #44

# Timing is everything.
## Agree upfront to a timeline:
## 'When will you get back to me?' or
## 'When should I follow up?'

*How important is this thumb-rule to you?* ☆ ☆ ☆ ☆ ☆

*What challenges prevent others from following this thumb-rule? Share it:*

ACTION ITEMS:

*How well do you practice this thumb-rule?* low 1 2 3 4 5 6 high

For explanations, anecdotes, and book recommendations,
go to *MarketingThumbrules.com* & type in these keyword tags:
Controls, time, planning, experience, questions

Ethical **Selling** Thumb–rule #45

# While nodding, affirm the expected response with, "Sounds great, right?"

*How important is this thumb-rule to you?* ☆ ☆ ☆ ☆ ☆

*What's your experience with this thumb-rule? Describe it here:*

---

ACTION ITEMS:

---

*How well do you practice this thumb-rule?* low 1 2 3 4 5 6 high

For explanations, anecdotes, and book recommendations, go to *MarketingThumbrules.com* & type in these keyword tags: Charisma, smile, results, questions

Ethical **Selling** Thumb-rule #46

# Take what you can get... upgrade the relationship later.

*How important is this thumb-rule to you?* ☆ ☆ ☆ ☆ ☆

*What challenges prevent others from following this thumb-rule? Share it:*

ACTION ITEMS:

*How well do you practice this thumb-rule?* low 1 2 3 4 5 6 high

For explanations, anecdotes, and book recommendations,
go to *MarketingThumbrules.com* & type in these keyword tags:
Controls, relationships, results, competition

Ethical **Selling** Thumb–rule #47

# Carry your appointment calendar.

*How important is this thumb-rule to you?* ☆ ☆ ☆ ☆ ☆

*What's your experience with this thumb-rule? Describe it here.*

ACTION ITEMS:

*How well do you practice this thumb-rule?* low  1  2  3  4  5  6  high

For explanations, anecdotes, and book recommendations,
go to *MarketingThumbrules.com* & type in these keyword tags:
Controls, time, networking, planning

Ethical **Selling** Thumb–rule #48

## Asking 5 consecutive 'why's' helps you get to the root cause.

*How important is this thumb-rule to you?* ☆ ☆ ☆ ☆ ☆

*What challenges prevent others from following this thumb-rule? Share it:*

..................................................................................................

..................................................................................................

..................................................................................................

..................................................................................................

ACTION ITEMS:

..................................................................................................

..................................................................................................

*How well do you practice this thumb-rule?* low  1   2   3   4   5   6  high

For explanations, anecdotes, and book recommendations,
go to *MarketingThumbrules.com* & type in these keyword tags:
Controls, mindset, presentation

Client **Appreciation** Thumb-rule #1

> # Thank them for their business.

*How important is this thumb-rule to you?* ☆ ☆ ☆ ☆ ☆

*What new ideas does this thumb-rule inspire? Write it here:*

---

---

---

---

ACTION ITEMS:

---

---

*How well do you practice this thumb-rule?* low 1 2 3 4 5 6 high

For explanations, anecdotes, and book recommendations,
go to *MarketingThumbrules.com* & type in these keyword tags:
Character, relationships, smile

Client **Appreciation** Thumb–rule #2

> # Value to our clients is a combination of Economic, Rational, & Emotional.

*How important is this thumb-rule to you?* ☆ ☆ ☆ ☆ ☆

*How will you use this thumb-rule today? Share it in the space below:*

ACTION ITEMS:

*How well do you practice this thumb-rule?* low 1  2  3  4  5  6  high

For explanations, anecdotes, and book recommendations,
go to *MarketingThumbrules.com* & type in these keyword tags:
Competency, Controls, experience, results

Client **Appreciation** Thumb–rule #3

## Ask for feedback.

*How important is this thumb-rule to you?* ☆ ☆ ☆ ☆ ☆

*What new ideas does this thumb-rule inspire? Write it here:*

ACTION ITEMS:

*How well do you practice this thumb-rule?* low 1  2  3  4  5  6  high

For explanations, anecdotes, and book recommendations,
go to *MarketingThumbrules.com* & type in these keyword tags:
Currency, questions, experience

Client **Appreciation** Thumb–rule #4

## Cross-sell, up-sell, and turn clients into affiliates.

*How important is this thumb-rule to you?* ☆ ☆ ☆ ☆ ☆

*How will you use this thumb-rule today? Share it in the space below:*

ACTION ITEMS:

*How well do you practice this thumb-rule?* low 1 2 3 4 5 6 high

For explanations, anecdotes, and book recommendations, go to *MarketingThumbrules.com* & type in these keyword tags: Channels, affiliates, money

Client **Appreciation** Thumb–rule #5

# Introduce your best, loyal clients to one another.

*How important is this thumb-rule to you?* ☆ ☆ ☆ ☆ ☆

*What new ideas does this thumb-rule inspire? Write it here:*

ACTION ITEMS:

*How well do you practice this thumb-rule?* low 1 2 3 4 5 6 high

For explanations, anecdotes, and book recommendations, go to *MarketingThumbrules.com* & type in these keyword tags: Community, relationships, networking, events

Client **Appreciation** Thumb–rule #6

# Remember birthdays and special interests.

*How important is this thumb-rule to you?* ☆ ☆ ☆ ☆ ☆

*How will you use this thumb-rule today? Share it in the space below:*

ACTION ITEMS:

*How well do you practice this thumb-rule?* low 1 2 3 4 5 6 high

For explanations, anecdotes, and book recommendations, go to *MarketingThumbrules.com* & type in these keyword tags: Charisma, Character, relationships, events

Client **Appreciation** Thumb-rule #7

## Use voicemail to record testimonials: Share recordings on your website.

*How important is this thumb-rule to you?* ☆ ☆ ☆ ☆ ☆

*What new ideas does this thumb-rule inspire? Write it here:*

---

---

---

---

ACTION ITEMS:

---

---

*How well do you practice this thumb-rule?* low 1 2 3 4 5 6 high

For explanations, anecdotes, and book recommendations, go to *MarketingThumbrules.com* & type in these keyword tags: Collaterals, Community, technology, relationships

Client **Appreciation** Thumb–rule #8

> ## People tell 10 people about a bad impression. Nobody talks about a regular experience. Folks tell 3 others about a great experience.

*How important is this thumb-rule to you?* ☆ ☆ ☆ ☆ ☆

*How will you use this thumb-rule today? Share it in the space below:*

ACTION ITEMS:

*How well do you practice this thumb-rule?* low 1 2 3 4 5 6 high

For explanations, anecdotes, and book recommendations, go to *MarketingThumbrules.com* & type in these keyword tags: Controls, Community, people, experience

Client **Appreciation** Thumb-rule #9

## Be willing to fire clients.

*How important is this thumb-rule to you?* ☆ ☆ ☆ ☆ ☆

*What new ideas does this thumb-rule inspire? Write it here:*

ACTION ITEMS:

*How well do you practice this thumb-rule?* low 1 2 3 4 5 6 high

For explanations, anecdotes, and book recommendations,
go to *MarketingThumbrules.com* & type in these keyword tags:
Controls, Channels, relationships, money, leadership

Client **Appreciation** Thumb–rule #10

## Categorize your notes and document progress with worksheets.

*How important is this thumb-rule to you?* ☆ ☆ ☆ ☆ ☆

*How will you use this thumb-rule today? Share it in the space below:*

ACTION ITEMS:

*How well do you practice this thumb-rule?* low  1  2  3  4  5  6  high

For explanations, anecdotes, and book recommendations,
go to *MarketingThumbrules.com* & type in these keyword tags:
Competency, Collaterals, system, results

Client **Appreciation** Thumb–rule #11

# Ask your clients how they get new clients.

*How important is this thumb-rule to you?* ☆ ☆ ☆ ☆ ☆

*What new ideas does this thumb-rule inspire? Write it here:*

-------------------------------------------------------------

-------------------------------------------------------------

-------------------------------------------------------------

-------------------------------------------------------------

ACTION ITEMS:

-------------------------------------------------------------

-------------------------------------------------------------

*How well do you practice this thumb-rule?* low  1   2   3   4   5   6   high

For explanations, anecdotes, and book recommendations,
go to *MarketingThumbrules.com* & type in these keyword tags:
Channels, questions, relationships

Client **Appreciation** Thumb-rule #12

> # Clients & colleagues forget quickly:
> # Continually remind them,
> # 'What have you done for me lately?'

*How important is this thumb-rule to you?* ☆ ☆ ☆ ☆ ☆

*How will you use this thumb-rule today? Share it in the space below:*

ACTION ITEMS:

*How well do you practice this thumb-rule?* low 1 2 3 4 5 6 high

For explanations, anecdotes, and book recommendations,
go to *MarketingThumbrules.com* & type in these keyword tags:
Controls, questions, results

Client **Appreciation** Thumb–rule #13

## Invoice ASAP, with a personal touch.

*How important is this thumb-rule to you?* ☆ ☆ ☆ ☆ ☆

*What new ideas does this thumb-rule inspire? Write it here:*

ACTION ITEMS:

*How well do you practice this thumb-rule?* low 1 2 3 4 5 6 high

For explanations, anecdotes, and book recommendations,
go to *MarketingThumbrules.com* & type in these keyword tags:
Controls, money, prioritize, relationships

Client **Appreciation** Thumb–rule #14

> # Credit cards help you collect on retainers more easily. The convenience is worth the fees.

*How important is this thumb-rule to you?* ☆ ☆ ☆ ☆ ☆

*How will you use this thumb-rule today? Share it in the space below:*

ACTION ITEMS:

*How well do you practice this thumb-rule?* low 1 2 3 4 5 6 high

For explanations, anecdotes, and book recommendations,
go to *MarketingThumbrules.com* & type in these keyword tags:
Controls, Currency, money

Client **Appreciation** Thumb-rule #15

## Ask a great client, "Do you know somebody that's just like you?"

*How important is this thumb-rule to you?* ☆ ☆ ☆ ☆ ☆

*What new ideas does this thumb-rule inspire? Write it here:*

ACTION ITEMS:

*How well do you practice this thumb-rule?* low 1 2 3 4 5 6 high

For explanations, anecdotes, and book recommendations, go to *MarketingThumbrules.com* & type in these keyword tags: Channels, questions, networking

Client **Appreciation** Thumb–rule #16

# Under promise, over deliver.

*How important is this thumb-rule to you?* ☆ ☆ ☆ ☆ ☆

*How will you use this thumb-rule today? Share it in the space below:*

ACTION ITEMS:

*How well do you practice this thumb-rule?* low 1  2  3  4  5  6  high

For explanations, anecdotes, and book recommendations,
go to *MarketingThumbrules.com* & type in these keyword tags:
Controls, results, experience

Client **Appreciation** Thumb–rule #17

---

**Write out check-lists for your clients.
Give it to prospects & colleagues.
(They'll share it with strangers.)**

---

*How important is this thumb-rule to you?* ☆ ☆ ☆ ☆ ☆

*What new ideas does this thumb-rule inspire? Write it here:*

------------------------------------------------

------------------------------------------------

------------------------------------------------

------------------------------------------------

ACTION ITEMS:

------------------------------------------------

------------------------------------------------

*How well do you practice this thumb-rule?* low 1 2 3 4 5 6 high

For explanations, anecdotes, and book recommendations,
go to *MarketingThumbrules.com* & type in these keyword tags:
Collaterals, Catchphrase, message, planning

Client **Appreciation** Thumb−rule #18

## Nominate clients for awards.

*How important is this thumb-rule to you?* ☆ ☆ ☆ ☆ ☆

*How will you use this thumb-rule today? Share it in the space below:*

ACTION ITEMS:

*How well do you practice this thumb-rule?* low 1 2 3 4 5 6 high

For explanations, anecdotes, and book recommendations,
go to *MarketingThumbrules.com* & type in these keyword tags:
Character, recognition, results

Client **Appreciation** Thumb-rule #19

> # Keep a client appreciation tactics check-off sheet (or CRM fields).

*How important is this thumb-rule to you?* ☆ ☆ ☆ ☆ ☆

*What new ideas does this thumb-rule inspire? Write it here:*

ACTION ITEMS:

*How well do you practice this thumb-rule?* low 1 2 3 4 5 6 high

For explanations, anecdotes, and book recommendations,
go to *MarketingThumbrules.com* & type in these keyword tags:
Collaterals, system, planning, goals, relationships, technology

Client **Appreciation** Thumb-rule #20

## Take a picture with your clients and link them on your website. Ask for a reciprocal link.

*How important is this thumb-rule to you?* ☆ ☆ ☆ ☆ ☆

*How will you use this thumb-rule today? Share it in the space below:*

ACTION ITEMS:

*How well do you practice this thumb-rule?* low 1 2 3 4 5 6 high

For explanations, anecdotes, and book recommendations, go to *MarketingThumbrules.com* & type in these keyword tags: Charisma, Collaterals, questions, technology

Client **Appreciation** Thumb-rule #21

# Have fun with your clients (e.g., golf, dinner, theatre, etc.).

*How important is this thumb-rule to you?* ☆ ☆ ☆ ☆ ☆

*What new ideas does this thumb-rule inspire? Write it here:*

ACTION ITEMS:

*How well do you practice this thumb-rule?* low 1 2 3 4 5 6 high

For explanations, anecdotes, and book recommendations, go to *MarketingThumbrules.com* & type in these keyword tags: Character, Channels, relationships, values

Client **Appreciation** Thumb-rule #22

> # If your clients are hesitant with referrals, ask them which associations they're active in. Ask if you can go along to the next event.

How important is this thumb-rule to you? ☆ ☆ ☆ ☆ ☆

How will you use this thumb-rule today? Share it in the space below:

ACTION ITEMS:

How well do you practice this thumb-rule? low 1 2 3 4 5 6 high

For explanations, anecdotes, and book recommendations, go to *MarketingThumbrules.com* & type in these keyword tags: Channels, questions, events, mindset

Client **Appreciation** Thumb–rule #23

> # If your client wants to work with a professional similiar to you, then ask them set up a get-together with the 3 of you.

*How important is this thumb-rule to you?* ☆ ☆ ☆ ☆ ☆

*What new ideas does this thumb-rule inspire? Write it here:*

ACTION ITEMS:

*How well do you practice this thumb-rule?* low 1 2 3 4 5 6 high

For explanations, anecdotes, and book recommendations, go to *MarketingThumbrules.com* & type in these keyword tags: Controls, competition, networking

Client **Appreciation** Thumb–rule #24

## Write out a meeting agenda. E-mail it beforehand (as a productive reminder).

*How important is this thumb-rule to you?* ☆ ☆ ☆ ☆ ☆

*How will you use this thumb-rule today? Share it in the space below:*

ACTION ITEMS:

*How well do you practice this thumb-rule?* low 1 2 3 4 5 6 high

For explanations, anecdotes, and book recommendations, go to *MarketingThumbrules.com* & type in these keyword tags: Collaterals, planning, technology

Client **Appreciation** Thumb–rule #25

## Quote your clients' expertise in your articles.

*How important is this thumb-rule to you?* ☆ ☆ ☆ ☆ ☆

*What new ideas does this thumb-rule inspire? Write it here:*

ACTION ITEMS:

*How well do you practice this thumb-rule?* low 1 2 3 4 5 6 high

For explanations, anecdotes, and book recommendations, go to *MarketingThumbrules.com* & type in these keyword tags: Competency, Collaterals, publishing, recognition, reputation

Your **Most Important** Thumb–rule #1

*How important is this thumb-rule to you?* ☆ ☆ ☆ ☆ ☆

*What's your experience with this thumb-rule? Write it below:*

ACTION ITEMS:

*How well do you practice this thumb-rule?* low 1 2 3 4 5 6 high

For explanations, anecdotes, and book recommendations,
copy the keyword tags here & go to *MarketingThumbrules.com*:

*We want your MTV...*
# Marketing Thumb-rules™ Volume

Remember the numbers you circled on the bottom of each page? "How well do you practice this thumb-rule?" Now, add up your Volume for each chapter. Then, add up your grand total. Next year, do it again. Go to **MarketingThumbrules.com** and see how you compare to other readers. And learn what your MTV says about you!

50 Thumb-rules for **Practice Management**: _____

58 Thumb-rules for **Market Positioning**: _____

86 Thumb-rules for **Personal Branding**: _____

98 Thumb-rules for **Professional Prospecting**: _____

48 Thumb-rules for **Ethical Selling**: _____

25 Thumb-rules for **Client Appreciation**: _____

**Add up your total MTV:** _____

*Leverage Your Personal Brand* is for today's savvy lawyers, accountants, financial planners, real estate, or health & wellness professionals: This audio-book is for those who know that it's no longer enough just to do a job-well-done.

Essentially, clients are buying you and your reputation, not just your services. Marketing and self-promotion – done ethically – is the only way your practice is going to grow. But your practice shouldn't be vulnerably co-dependent on your time or reputation. Rather, you must *leverage* your personal brand.

Recorded live, *Leverage Your Personal Brand* is a 2-disc audio-book chock-full of practical insight. Vikram Rajan first presents the Personal Brand Formula™ and then showcases the full Spectrum of personal branding. From there, Vik takes us through each of the Formula components, offering practical advice and tips.

The bulk of the program is on specific marketing communication tactics: Vikram highlights how to best design your marketing materials (collaterals) to bring out your personal brand distinctiveness. Vik also explains how to effectively prospect through 7 marketing channels.

Furthermore, Vikram then helps us understand how we can leverage our good name, good will, and reputation in the marketplace. Vik offers insight into effective delegation, systemization, knowledge product development, and leadership. You'll want to listen to this 2-disc audio-book over and over again. And then gift it to a friend!

There is a companion workbook, but it is optional for this audio-book. Please go to MarketingThumbrules.com to purchase your copies of the 2-disc *Leverage Your Personal Brand* audio-book!

*INSTANT BUZZ*: 6 Free Ways to Get More Referrals! The title just about says it all. Like most other professionals, your practice grows mostly through word-of-mouth referrals. But how can you encourage others to buzz about you even more?

If you're an avid networker at chambers of commerce, private roundtables, events, or tradeshows, then you must implement the lessons of *INSTANT BUZZ!* Make your valuable time even more productive.

Based on the concept of Currency, Vikram Rajan gives us examples of how we can use 6 specific "buzz streams." By updating our own personal brand marketing with this currency, we will be able to tap into our market's trends, forces, and "water cooler" conversations. In this way, we can ride the waves to even greater word-of-mouth success.

While there is a lot of insight on this 1 CD, you need not be overwhelmed. Vik shows us how each of the 6 buzz streams can stand alone, or work together for even more impressive results. In fact, as you put these buzz streams to use, your circle of influence will talk about you to the right prospects – and recommend that they call you immediately.

*INSTANT BUZZ* is a 60-minute audio-book, with an optional workbook. It has been designed for you to lisen in the car, but it's best studied when you can take notes. *INSTANT BUZZ* is a classic recording by Vikram Rajan: He talks fast, with passion and wit.

If you know of colleagues who feel networking isn't paying off, then gift this audio-book to them. Please go to MarketingThumbrules.com to purchase your copies of the audio-book, *INSTANT BUZZ*: 6 Free Ways to Get More Referrals!

Shy, Quiet, Introverted? Get what you want with ease, with *MAGNETIC PERSONALITY!*

Vikram Rajan is often complimented for his people skills. But in reality, in many social situations, Vik can be shy and introverted. Vik's amazing way to relate to people, on and off stage, have all been developed over time. You toocan learn how to create a *MAGNETIC PERSONALITY!*

In this audio-book, Vikram first talks about how we can immediately stand out and be remembered in any crowd. Charisma is the way we develop rapport with others beyond what we have in common. Vikram explains how we can use the 3 levels of Charisma: acting, basing, and cooperating. Vik gives multiple thumb-rules on how to act charismatically. He then shows how we can base our *MAGNETIC PERSONALITY* on our natural talents and behavior.

Ultimately, charisma is spiritual: How can we obey our law of attraction? Moreover, how can we improve our personal brand through our Role Model Collage? Vik walks us through a simple, fun exercise – that you can also use to build team rapport and even family relationships.

Vikram concludes this 60-minute audio-book by giving quick thumb-rules to make our presentations and interpersonal communication more influential. You can relate to anybody, anywhere, any time, with *MAGNETIC PERSONALITY!*

You're going to want to listen to Vik's upbeat, inspirational, and practical audio-book over and over again. And then gift it to a friend. Please go to MarketingThumbrules.com to order your copies of *MAGNETIC PERSONALITY:* Get what you want with ease.

Meet more prospects who will practically close themselves, and achieve *SALES MOMENTUM!*

Sorry, this isn't about closing techniques or about your sales funnel. In fact, it's better than that: Do you know who Peter Drucker is? He is the father of modern-day management science. Peter Drucker says, "The aim of marketing is to know and understand the customer so well [that] the product or service fits him and sells itself."

*SALES MOMENTUM*, another audio-book by Vikram Rajan, will help you discover the power of focusing on an overlooked and frustrated Community, a tight-knit target market population who tends recommend services catering to their peculiar needs.

While his INSTANT BUZZ audio-book showcases how we market, *SALES MOMENTUM* focuses upon whom we market (together, they're a powerful combination). By understanding who belongs in our target market – and who doesn't – we can better market to their needs and desires. We can also predict where they will be, when they'll be there, with whom they do business, how they make decisions, and when they'll buy from us: WOW!

Through examples and exercises, Vik walks us through the 6 criteria to create a momentum of word-of-mouth referrals, as shown through the optional companion workbook. Vikram then helps you hone your personal brand to appeal more powerfully to your target market Community. With or without the workbook, you'll want to study this audio-book and take notes.

Please go to MarketingThumbrules.com to order your copies of *SALES MOMENTUM*: Meet more prospects who'll close themselves.

Ultimately, your success depends on Your Marketing *TIME MANAGEMENT.* In this practical audio-book, Vikram Rajan helps us to realize what robs us of our time, and how to get the most out of our most precious resource.

When is the right time to develop our marketing collaterals? When is the best time to leave messages, or get around gatekeepers? When is the best time to speak with our prospects? When is the best time to schedule our seminars and events? When is the best time to plan for the future? It's all answered in Your Marketing *TIME MANAGEMENT!*

Vik helps us install a simple mechanism to prioritize, delegate, and/ or delete certain tasks from our to-do list. He then helps us develop a more strategic map that can be kept up-to-date through weekly planning.

Moreover, Vikram offers us a model marketing calendar that is relevant for lawyers, accountants, financial planners, real estate, and health & wellness professionals. Vik helps us design our 1000-day vision and then a practical 300-day calendar. He then helps us refine it to become monthly marketing action plans (MAPs). In this way, we can sustain effective day-to-day *TIME MANAGEMENT,* yet stay in alignment with our long-term plans.

Your Marketing *TIME MANAGEMENT* also helps us replace our ineffective habits with the right ones to achieve our brand of success. As we develop the right habits, our actions pattern become second nature. We no longer have to remember or even schedule our critical tasks = LESS STRESS & MORE LEVERAGE!

Please go to MarketingThumbrules.com to order your copies of Your Marketing *TIME MANAGEMENT*: Achieve your vision.

Prospect like Craigslist, YouTube, eBay, blogging, podcasting, and more!

You've probably heard the term Web 2.0, but how can you use it to generate prospects?

In *WEB MARKETING 2.0*, Vikram Rajan showcases the 6 kinds of websites that you should host (and improve). And 7 ways (the only seven ways) to drive more traffic to your websites.

First of all, Vik gives you quick thumb-rules to improve your basic website. Then, Vik highlights the basics of Search Engine Optimization (SEO). Vikram then gives you tips to become active in your target market's on-line communities, and finally how to start developing your own interactive community (on and off-line).

Transform your archaic "brochure website" into an engaging and effective prospecting channel. Even if you don't expect prospects to find you directly through your website, *WEB MARKETING 2.0* will help your centers of influence, clients, and prospects to recommend you with more energy. Nowadays, it's simple to make your websites more interactive and interesting with "copy & paste" multimedia widgets.

In the next few years, blogs, podcasts, and video will be as everyday as a professional website. But right now, it's novel and cutting-edge: *WEB MARKETING 2.0* will set your practice apart. Vik concludes with 10½ free ways to grow your e-newsletter list without spamming!

Already savvy? But know of colleagues trapped in the 20th century? Gift this audio-book to them! Please go to MarketingThumbrules.com to order your copies of *WEB MARKETING 2.0*: Prospect like Craigslist, YouTube, and eBay.

# Are we missing a Marketing Thumb-rule™?

Go on-line to MarketingThumbrules.com and add your own thumb-rules. The best ones will be included in Volume 2, etc. Of course, you will be thanked in the book for your input.

Please do not include quotes, copyrighted statements, or clichés. There is a difference between cliché truisms and what we consider thumb-rules:

A cliché is an often-repeated phrase, and often true. A rule-of-thumb, however, is a measurement or measurable action. (It may also be cliché, but not necessarily.)

As you can see from this book, thumb-rules are actionable or directly imply what to do (or what not to do). Here's 1 thumb-rule for writing thumb-rules: Start with a verb (or adverb). We all look forward to your additions.

Search the blog at MarketingThumbrules.com with the keyword tags associated with the thumb-rules (at the bottom of each page). You'll get to read more insight into the thumb-rule, read book recommendations, and read other people's comments. Feel free to add your comments to any blog post.

While you're at MarketingThumbrules.com, compare your Marketing Thumb-rules Volume (MTV) with other readers. You can also learn how your score impacts your practice development. Next year, watch how your volume has grown.

As you can see, there are plenty of reasons to subscribe to the newsletter updates at MarketingThumbrules.com. The most important reason, though, is that we're missing a few thumb-rules. And only you know what those are!

## *Brand your name with your own custom cover!*

Check out the cover again: Your name can appear on top. Your custom branded book will be an impressive gift, promotional tool, and networking resource.

Take this book to your next networking group, organization meeting, or chamber of commerce event. Watch how you and your insights immediately become the center of attention.

Moreover, notice how the conversation becomes focused on effective marketing techniques. Members will open up with ideas, examples, and referrals. Relationships will grow.

Now imagine how memorable you will be with a branded book: With the printing technology we use, CoGrow can have your business, organization or personal name printed right on the cover of this book: Just order 15 copies (or more) at a time!

Feel free to either gift copies to your colleagues, or use this book as a fundraiser. Like you, colleagues will cherish this book as a daily reminder. Thus, they will think of you everyday.

**To order more copies of this book, with or without a custom cover, go to <u>MarketingThumbrules.com</u>. For more information, call CoGrow at 516.642.4100.**

You can also invite the author, Vikram Rajan, to present and facilitate group discussions around the right set Marketing Thumb-rules for your members. Vik will help your members share their own experiences, expertise, and excitement.

Read the author's biography, or his podBlog, to learn more about Vik's experience working with professional associations.

## ABOUT VIKRAM RAJAN

Vikram Rajan is the co-founder of CoGrow Systems, Inc., a business development firm for small-business owners. Vik also authors the podBlog, **ViksMarketingBlog.com**, which receives over 300 views everyday.

Vik is a Personal Brand Marketing Advisor™ for lawyers, accountants, financial planners, real estate, and health & wellness professionals.

Vikram's marketing columns appear in more than 14 publications, including Financial Advisor magazine, Dominican Times magazine, Times-Ledger newspapers, Personal Branding magazine, and more. Vik also wrote the business column for Long Island Business News. Vik has taught for the Fashion Institute of Technology, Dowling College, and is to teach for C.W. Post, Long Island University.

Vik has also been quoted by the Wall Street Journal's Startup Journal, Entrepreneurship magazine, Channel Pro, and more. In January 2004, Vikram was named a "Top 40 Under 40 Rising Star" by Long Island Business News.

Vik co-chairs the Membership and the Business Development committees for the Hauppauge Industrial Association (HIA), Long Island's 2nd largest business organization. Vikram also serves on the Board of Managers for the Cross Island YMCA, and has been invited to participate on a special marketing committee for the YMCA of Greater New York.

Vik has presented in front of many networking groups & organizations: U.S. Small Business Administration (SBA) • Nassau County Bar Association (Academy of Law) • National Network of Accountants • National Association of Insurance and Financial Advisors (Queens) • National Conference of CPA Practitioners (Suffolk) • Association of Divorce Financial Planners • Independent Real Esate Brokers • Direct Marketing Association of Long Island • Long Island Hispanic Chamber of Commerce, and many, many, many banks!

Vikram is an activist for the ethical treament of all animals, including humans. When you invite him, remember he is a vegetarian! E-mail him at Vik@CoGrow.com; Vikram Rajan currently lives on Long Island.

Printed in the United States
210442BV00008B/7/A